Help yourself to
# *algebra*

## Hugh Neill

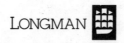
LONGMAN

Longman Group Limited
Edinburgh Gate, Burnt Mill, Harlow,
Essex CM20 2JE, England
and Associated Companies throughout the world.

First published 1996

Set in Times
Produced by Longman Singapore Publishers (Pte) Ltd
Printed in Singapore

ISBN  0 582 29068 6

The publisher's policy is to use paper manufactured
from sustainable forests.

# Contents

# Preface

Many teachers and lecturers claim that their students do not have enough skill in algebra as they start advanced courses in mathematics. This book is intended to enable students to improve their algebraic skills, and by doing so, increase their confidence when applying it to other parts of mathematics, or to problems or modelling.

There are plenty of exercises in this book. The purpose of the exercises is to give practice in manipulation and equation solving. The exercises are graded, and most types of exercise have a worked example with a full commentary to provide assistance.

I have made extensive use of the text of New General Mathematics in this publication. I wish to thank the authors J B Channon and H C Head and the estate of the late A McLeish Smith for permission to do so. I would also like to thank Sue Maunder for checking the manuscript and Longman Education for their speed in producing this book.

While many of the exercises were taken from New General Mathematics, the responsibility for any errors is mine.

Hugh Neill
June 29, 1995

# 1 How to use this book

**Assumptions made**

This is not a book about applications or about problems. It is a book designed to help you with algebraic manipulation.

The assumption is that you are not a beginner, and that you have been taught some algebra, but forgotten it, or you need to improve it for some reason, such as more advanced study of mathematics.

**Learning a technique**

Suppose that you need to learn how to carry out a particular technique. Look for the chapter which includes the technique, and study the worked examples carefully, preferably with a pen in your hand.

Write down the steps as you go, and check each step carefully. Ask yourself: why was this particular step chosen? Do I agree with the working? Why is it like that?

Remember that mathematics is not disconnected, and if you can learn general principles of how to do algebra, you will make better progress.

**Try the exercises**

If you get stuck with a particular problem, then look back at a worked example similar to the one you are having difficulty with, and try to isolate the place where you are having difficulty.

Look at the answer. Sometimes, but not always, the general form of the answer can give you a clue. Remember that sometimes there can be different forms of the same answer, and it may be that your answer is correct, but you may not recognise it as correct.

There are plenty of exercises in the book. Do as many as you need to perfect a technique. There is no point in doing more questions just because they are there!

## Short cuts

In many cases the examples are worked in more detail than you need to give in a solution. If you can skip lines, do so; but don't make errors by doing it! It is better to write more steps, and to get the solution correct, than to skip steps, get things wrong and subsequently lose confidence.

# 2    Making things simpler

One of the processes most frequently needed in algebra is to make complicated algebraic expressions simpler. Mathematicians use the somewhat awkward word 'simplify' for this process.

It is important that at each stage the simplified expression is the same as the original expression.

Here are some examples. Remember that $2x$ means $2 \times x$.

**1**    Simplify $2x + 7x$.

|  |  |
|---|---|
| This is an example of adding like terms. | $2x + 7x$<br>$= 9x$ |

**2**    Simplify $3m - 9m - 2m + 16m$.

|  |  |
|---|---|
| This is only a bigger version of the first example. | $3m - 9m - 2m + 16m$<br>$= 8m$ |

Remember that terms like $3x$ and 4 are 'unlike' and that $3x + 4$ cannot be simplified further.

**3**    Simplify $7h - 4 - 3h + 11$.

|  |  |
|---|---|
| Collect the terms with $h$, and the numbers separately. | $7h - 4 - 3h + 11$<br>$= 4h + 7$ |

**4**    Simplify $7x + 3y - 4 + 2x - y$.

|  |  |
|---|---|
| Collect the terms with $x$, $y$ and the numbers separately. | $7x + 3y - 4 + 2x - y$<br>$= 9x + 2y - 4$ |

Remember that $ab$ means $a \times b$.

**5**   Simplify $3xy + 4xy$.

|  |  |
|---|---|
| Collect the like terms in $xy$. | $3xy + 4xy$<br>$= 7xy$ |

Remember that when you multiply three numbers, it doesn't matter in which order you multiply them. This means that $6vu$, which means $6 \times v \times u$ is the same as $6uv$, so that terms in $uv$ and $vu$ are like terms. Although there is no need to do so, it can make like terms easier to recognize if you write the letters in alphabetical order.

**6**   Simplify $8uv - 6vu$.

|  |  |
|---|---|
| It doesn't matter whether you give $2uv$ or $2vu$ as answer. | $8uv - 6vu$<br>$= 2uv$ |

**7**   Simplify $9ab + 4bc - 5ba + 3bc$.

|  |  |
|---|---|
| The terms in $ab$ and $bc$ are not like terms so they cannot be simplified further. | $9ab + 4bc - 5ba + 3bc$<br>$= 4ab + 7bc$ |

Indices are used to write expressions like $xx$, which means $x \times x$, as $x^2$. Similarly $x^3$ means $x \times x \times x$. Using this notation $xy^2$ means $x \times y \times y$.

**8**   Simplify $3a^2 - 2a + a^3 - a^2$.

|  |  |
|---|---|
| Only the terms with the same powers are like terms. | $3a^2 - 2a + a^3 - a^2$<br>$= 2a^2 - 2a + a^3$ |

**9** Simplify $7 \times 3a - 25a + 5a \times 2$.

As in arithmetic, multiplication (and division) must be carried out before addition and subtraction.

Collect like terms.

$$7 \times 3a - 25a + 5a \times 2$$
$$= 21a - 25a + 10a$$

$$= 6a$$

**10** Simplify $4a \times 3 - 1$.

$$4a \times 3 - 1$$

Multiply first, giving $12a$, and then it will not simplify further.

$$12a - 1$$

## *Exercise 2*

Simplify the following expressions, where possible.

**1** $6d + d$

**2** $8e + 5e - 7e$

**3** $11n - 3n - 6n + 9n - 5n$

**4** $9a + 10b - 5a + 4b$

**5** $8h - 3 - 5h + 9$

**6** $7x + 5y - 4$

**7** $11x + 9y - 7x$

**8** $13a + 2b - 9a + 7b$

**9** $5f - 3g - 7f + 9g + 3f - 4g$

**10** $7m - 2n + 6 - 5m + 7n + 3$

**11** $3x + 2 - 7x - 4 + 5x + 6$

**12** $a - 7b + 3c + 8b + 2a$

**13** $5h + 8k + 2 - 3k - 2h$

**14** $6m + 3n - 1 - 6m + 4$

**15** $a - 2b - 4a + 3c + 4a + 5b$

**16** $6p - 2q + 4r - 6p + 3s + 5q$

**17** $3xy + 4xy$

**18** $9ab - 5ab$

**19** $17hk - 9kh$

**20** $10ab + 7bc$

**21** $7cd - 8dc + 3cd$

**22** $9xy + 5yx - 13xy$

**23** $4ab + 10bc - ab - 7cb$

**24** $5ab - 2ab + 3bc - ba$

**25** $7fg + 8gf - 9fg + 3gh$

**26** $5uv - 2vw - 3vu + 4vw - uv$

**27** $3ab - bc + 5cd + 3cb - 4dc$

**28** $4mn + 7mn - 8mu - 6vu$

**29** $8ab - 3cd - 5ba + 5cd + 2ac$

**30** $7p - 2q + 4r - 3p - r + 2s$

**31** $3a^2 + 6a + 5 + 2a^2 + a + 3$

**32** $2b^2 + 3b + 5 + 4b^2 - b - 4$

**33** $8c^2 - 2c + 7 - 6c^2 + 5c - 2$

**34** $5x^2 + 6x - 4x^2 - x + 3$

**35** $y^2 - 3 + 9y + 6y^2 - 5y + 6$

**36** $4z^3 + 8z - 3 + 5z^2 + 7 - 2z^3$

**37** $3m \times 5$

**38** $4 \times 8a$

**39** $7h \times 3$

**40** $\frac{1}{4}$ of $20k$

**41** $28x \div 7$

**42** $3n \times 2 + 5n$

**43** $4 \times 5p - 3p$

**44** $4a \times 3 + 5$

**45** $2 \times 7b - 3$

**46** $3 + 2 \times 5m$

**47** $4x + 3x \times 3$

**48** $17y - 5y \times 2$

**49** $21 - 2 \times 7a$

**50** $8m \times 0$

**51** $3a \times 1$

**52** $5t + 1$

**53** $4 \times 8x - 7x \times 3$

**54** $\frac{1}{3}$ of $15ab$

**55** $21mn \div 3$

**56** $6u \times 4 - 2 \times 7u$

**57** $2 \times x \times 3 \times y$

**58** $p \times q \times 0$

**59** $3a \times 4b$

**60** $3a + 4b$

**61** $pq + 0$

**62** $7x - 3 \times 4x + 5x \times 2$

**63** $28cd \times \frac{1}{4}$

**64** $m \times 5 \times m \times 3$

**65** $4n \times 7n$

**66** $6u \times 5 + 3 \times 4u - 2u$

**67** $7v \times 2 + 5 \times 8v - 6v \times 9$

**68** $5 \times 6a - 4a \times 0 - 4a \times 7$

# 3 Fractions

In algebra, letters represent numbers. You must therefore expect to encounter and manipulate fractions, just as you would with numbers.

The rules about cancelling are the same as with numbers. If you find yourself in difficulties, ask yourself what you would do in a similar situation involving numbers.

**1** Express $\dfrac{6ab}{15ac}$ in its lowest terms.

$$\dfrac{6ab}{15ac}$$

Divide both the numerator and denominator by $3a$. The fraction is now in its lowest terms.

$$\dfrac{2b}{5c}$$

**2** Express $\dfrac{dx}{d^2}$ in its lowest terms.

$$\dfrac{dx}{d^2}$$

Divide both the numerator and denominator by $d$. The fraction is now in its lowest terms.

$$\dfrac{x}{d}$$

You can also add and subtract algebraic fractions exactly as you would with numbers.

**3** Put $\dfrac{3a}{5} - \dfrac{8b}{5}$ over a common denominator.

$$\dfrac{3a}{5} - \dfrac{8b}{5}$$

The two denominators are the same, 5. So you simply subtract the numerators.

$$\dfrac{3a}{5} - \dfrac{8b}{5} = \dfrac{3a - 8b}{5}$$

**4**  Put $\dfrac{9}{5ab} - \dfrac{8}{5ab}$ over a common denominator.

$$\dfrac{9}{5ab} - \dfrac{8}{5ab}$$

The two denominators are the same, $5ab$. So you simply subtract the numerators.

$$\dfrac{9}{5ab} - \dfrac{8}{5ab} = \dfrac{1}{5ab}$$

If the denominators are not the same, then you must express them with the same denominator, using the least common multiple, LCM.

**5**  Put $\dfrac{5a}{6} - \dfrac{2b}{9}$ over a common denominator.

$$\dfrac{5a}{6} - \dfrac{2b}{9}$$

The LCM is 18. Then you get the following expression.

$$\dfrac{5a}{6} - \dfrac{2b}{9} = \dfrac{3 \times 5a - 2 \times 2b}{18}$$

The numerator of this expression then simplifies.

$$\dfrac{15a - 4b}{18}$$

**6**  Put $\dfrac{d}{ab} - \dfrac{e}{bc}$ over a common denominator.

$$\dfrac{d}{ab} - \dfrac{e}{bc}$$

The LCM is $abc$. Then you get the following expression.

$$\dfrac{d}{ab} - \dfrac{e}{bc} = \dfrac{c \times d - a \times e}{abc}$$

The numerator of this expression then simplifies.

$$\dfrac{cd - ae}{abc}$$

When you multiply and divide fractions the rules are again the same as for numbers.

**7** Simplify $\dfrac{4ab}{9} \times \dfrac{6m}{acm}$.

$$\dfrac{4ab}{9} \times \dfrac{6m}{acm}$$

Start by cancelling the numbers.

$$\dfrac{4ab}{9} \times \dfrac{6m}{acm} = \dfrac{8}{3} \times \dfrac{abm}{acm}$$

Now divide the numerator and denominator by $am$.

$$\dfrac{8b}{3c}$$

**8** Simplify $\dfrac{16cd}{21mn} \div \dfrac{24c}{35n}$.

$$\dfrac{16cd}{21mn} \div \dfrac{24c}{35n}$$

Start by using the same technique as with numbers.

$$\dfrac{16cd}{21mn} \times \dfrac{35n}{24c}$$

Then cancel the numbers.

$$\dfrac{16cd}{21mn} \times \dfrac{35n}{24c} = \dfrac{10}{9} \times \dfrac{cdn}{mnc}$$

Now divide the numerator and denominator by $nc$.

$$\dfrac{10d}{9m}$$

## Exercise 3

Express the following fractions in their lowest terms.

**1** $\dfrac{3a}{8a}$      **2** $\dfrac{5m}{7m}$      **3** $\dfrac{2x}{10x}$

**4** $\dfrac{12a}{16a}$      **5** $\dfrac{4b}{12b}$      **6** $\dfrac{9e}{12e}$

**7** $\dfrac{2mx}{8my}$      **8** $\dfrac{16ab}{20bc}$      **9** $\dfrac{7abc}{21bc}$

**10** $\dfrac{8dk}{12dh}$ **11** $\dfrac{42a^2}{56a}$ **12** $\dfrac{15m}{20mn}$

**13** $\dfrac{24amx}{30anx}$ **14** $\dfrac{108x}{144x^2}$ **15** $\dfrac{xyz^2}{xy^2z}$

Put each of the following fractions over a common denominator.

**16** $\dfrac{5a}{11}+\dfrac{3a}{11}$ **17** $\dfrac{5b}{8}-\dfrac{3b}{8}$ **18** $\dfrac{2c}{5}+\dfrac{4c}{5}$

**19** $\dfrac{3x}{4}+\dfrac{x}{6}$ **20** $\dfrac{2m}{3}-\dfrac{3n}{5}$ **21** $\dfrac{5a}{6}-\dfrac{3b}{8}$

**22** $\dfrac{a}{m}+\dfrac{2b}{m}$ **23** $\dfrac{5x}{a}-\dfrac{3y}{a}$ **24** $\dfrac{7}{mn}+\dfrac{3}{mn}$

**25** $\dfrac{2c}{uvw}+\dfrac{3d}{uvw}$ **26** $\dfrac{4a}{5}-\dfrac{3b}{10}+\dfrac{c}{2}$ **27** $\dfrac{3a}{4}+\dfrac{a}{3}-\dfrac{5a}{6}$

**28** $\dfrac{a}{2}-\dfrac{2b}{3}+\dfrac{3c}{4}$ **29** $a+\dfrac{x}{4}$ **30** $\dfrac{5a}{12}-\dfrac{3c}{8}$

**31** $\dfrac{c}{4}+\dfrac{2d}{3}-\dfrac{5e}{6}$ **32** $u-\dfrac{2d}{5}$ **33** $\dfrac{4}{m}-\dfrac{3}{n}$

**34** $\dfrac{m}{2a}-\dfrac{n}{3a}$ **35** $\dfrac{2}{au}-\dfrac{5}{bu}$ **36** $\dfrac{4}{ac}+\dfrac{3}{ce}$

**37** $\dfrac{3}{mn}+\dfrac{5}{mx}-\dfrac{2}{nx}$ **38** $\dfrac{p}{ab}-\dfrac{q}{ac}+\dfrac{r}{bc}$ **39** $\dfrac{4a}{9}\times\dfrac{3}{2}$

**40** $\dfrac{5a}{6}\times\dfrac{9}{a}$ **41** $\dfrac{6m}{4a}\times\dfrac{12}{m}$ **42** $\dfrac{7x}{12}\times\dfrac{9}{14}$

**43** $\dfrac{5}{24}\times\dfrac{16m}{15}$ **44** $\dfrac{20}{27e}\times\dfrac{18m}{25}$ **45** $\dfrac{16h}{21k}\times\dfrac{35k}{32m}$

**46** $\dfrac{21am}{4}\times\dfrac{3}{7m}$ **47** $\dfrac{9abc}{10a}\times\dfrac{16m}{21b^2}$ **48** $\dfrac{18am^2x}{5}\times\dfrac{5}{6my}$

**49** $\dfrac{4x}{5}\div\dfrac{12x}{35}$ **50** $\dfrac{15}{8a}\div\dfrac{5}{6a}$ **51** $\dfrac{3ab}{14}\div\dfrac{12b}{7}$

**52** $\dfrac{8a}{5mn}\div\dfrac{32b}{15mn}$

# 4  Brackets

The terms inside a bracket are meant to be taken as a whole. However, there are times when you need to remove brackets.

When you remove brackets:

- if you multiply or divide a bracket by a positive number, the signs of all the terms inside the brackets remain unchanged;

- if you multiply or divide a bracket by a negative number, you must change the signs of all the terms inside the brackets;

- if there are brackets inside other brackets, start by removing the innermost brackets.

**1**  Remove the brackets and simplify $7g + (3g - 4h) - (2g - 9h)$.

|  |  |
|---|---|
|  | $7g + (3g - 4h) - (2g - 9h)$ |
| The second bracket is multiplied by $-1$, so all the signs change. | $7g + 3g - 4h - 2g + 9h$ |
| Now simplify by collecting like terms. | $8g + 5h$ |

A long line over the top of an expression counts as a bracket.

**2**  Remove the brackets and simplify $\overline{6x - y - 3z} - \overline{2x + 5y - 4z}$.

|  |  |
|---|---|
|  | $\overline{6x - y - 3z} - \overline{2x + 5y - 4z}$ |
| The second bracket is multiplied by $-1$, so all the signs change. | $6x - y - 3z - 2x - 5y + 4z$ |
| Now simplify by collecting like terms. | $4x - 6y + z$ |

**3**    Remove the brackets and simplify $3(a+2b)-2(a-3b)$.

$$3(a+2b)-2(a-3b)$$

The second bracket is multiplied by $-2$, so all the signs change.

$$3a+6b-2a+6b$$

Now simplify by collecting like terms.

$$a+12b$$

**4**    Remove the brackets and simplify $2\times\overline{p+2q-3r}-3\times\overline{3p+2q}$.

$$2\times\overline{p+2q-3r}-3\times\overline{3p+2q}$$

The second bracket is multiplied by $-3$, so all the signs change.

$$2p+4q-6r-9p-6q$$

Now simplify by collecting like terms.

$$-7p-2q-6r$$

**5**    Remove the brackets and simplify $2x-\left[3x-\{(x+4)-(2x-3)\}\right]$.

$$2x-\left[3x-\{(x+4)-(2x-3)\}\right]$$

Start with the innermost brackets.

$$=2x-\left[3x-\{x+4-2x+3\}\right]$$

Simplify in the inside bracket.

$$=2x-\left[3x-\{-x+7\}\right]$$

Remove the next bracket.

$$=2x-\left[3x+x-7\right]$$

Simplify.

$$=2x-\left[4x-7\right]$$

And so on.

$$=2x-4x+7$$

$$=-2x+7$$

**6**   Remove the brackets and simplify $ab - 2a^2 + 2\{a^2 - 2(ab - 3b^2)\}$.

Start with the innermost brackets. 

$$ab - 2a^2 + 2\{a^2 - 2(ab - 3b^2)\}$$

$$= ab - 2a^2 + 2\{a^2 - 2ab + 6b^2\}$$

Remove the next bracket.

$$= ab - 2a^2 + 2a^2 - 4ab + 12b^2$$

Simplify.

$$= -3ab + 12b^2$$

# *Exercise 4*

Rewrite the following expressions without brackets.

**1**   $h + (k - m + n)$      **2**   $h - (k + m - n)$

**3**   $a - \overline{b - c}$      **4**   $5a + \overline{b - 5c}$

**5**   $4x - (3y + 2)$      **6**   $6 - p - (3q - 7r)$

**7**   $3m + \overline{6h - k} - 5n$      **8**   $(4a - b) + (3c - 7)$

**9**   $4a - (5x - 2y) + 3b$      **10**   $(3e + f) - (2g - h)$

In each of the following, remove the brackets and simplify.

**11**   $7a - (5a + 2b)$      **12**   $5m - (m - 3n)$

**13**   $4x + \overline{y - x}$      **14**   $7x - \overline{8x - 5y}$

**15**   $8m + (3n - 8m)$      **16**   $u + 3v + (2u - 3v)$

**17**   $8u - \overline{6u + 3v} - 2v$      **18**   $6a - (4 - a) - 3$

**19**   $(4m + 6) - (6m + 8)$      **20**   $(4u - v + w) + (u - 2v - w)$

**21**   $4a^2 + 3a - 1 - 2a^2 - 4a + 3$      **22**   $(3x - 5y + 1) - (4x + y - 3)$

**23**   $(p - q) - (p + q) + (p - q)$      **24**   $(5a + 3b) + (a - 3b) - 6a - b$

**25**   $\overline{xy - yz} - yx - zw$

**26**   $2a^2 - (1 + a^2) - 7a + (a + 7)$      **27**   $(4 + a) - (6 + 2b) + (5 - 3c)$

**28**   $(3g - 2h) + (4h - 3k) - (5k - 4g)$

**29**   $(e^2 + 4e) - (2e - 3) - (5 + 3e^2)$

**30**   $4lm - 5mn - 6nl + 3lm - 5ln - 4nm$

Rewrite the following expressions without brackets.

**3 1** $3(u+v+w)$        **3 2** $-4(l-m-n)$

**3 3** $2 \times \overline{x+3y+2z}$        **3 4** $5(3a+b-2c)$

**3 5** $3(5p-2q-3r+4s)$        **3 6** $-3(2c+3d-5)$

**3 7** $\frac{1}{2}(2u-8v+6)$        **3 8** $\frac{3}{4}(12c-20d-4e)$

**3 9** $2(3m+n)-3(u+2v)$        **4 0** $5(3a-4b)+2(3c+5d)$

In each of the following, remove the brackets and simplify.

**4 1** $3a+2(a+2b)$        **4 2** $6x+3(2y-x)$

**4 3** $7u-5(u-v)$        **4 4** $5d-3 \times \overline{e+2d}$

**4 5** $5m-8n+5(2n-m)$        **4 6** $11u-3 \times \overline{3u+2v}$

**4 7** $2(a-3b)+3(a+b)$        **4 8** $4 \times 3m-2$

**4 9** $4(3m-2)$        **5 0** $2(h+5k)+5(h+2k)$

**5 1** $2(b+2c)+3(b-2c)$        **5 2** $6(a-2b)-3(2a+b)$

**5 3** $4(x-2y)-3(2x-y)$        **5 4** $5 \times \overline{u+3v}-3 \times \overline{u+4v}$

**5 5** $5a-7b-4(a-2b+c)$        **5 6** $a+3(2a+3b-c)-c$

**5 7** $3(4a-8b+1)-4(3a-6b+1)$

**5 8** $4 \times \overline{m+n}-3 \times \overline{3m-2n}+5 \times \overline{m-2n}$

**5 9** $4 \times 3a-b-3 \times 2a+b$

**6 0** $3(2u-v)-4(v+2w)-5(w+2u)$

**6 1** $2[(x+2)+(x+3)]$        **6 2** $3\{(3x-5)-(2x-6)\}$

**6 3** $5(2x+5-\overline{3x-2})$        **6 4** $4[2(2x+1)-3(x-2)]$

**6 5** $[x(x-2y)-2y(x+y)]$        **6 6** $3\{a(a+b)+b(a+b)\}$

# 5  Fractions with brackets

The notation where the horizontal line acts as a bracket, for example, in $\overline{x+y}$ is useful when you come to work with fractions like $\dfrac{x+3}{4}$. The fraction line acts as a bracket, a fact that you need to remember when you are working with fractions.

**1**  Express $\dfrac{3(2x-y)}{8} - \dfrac{x+2y}{8}$ as a single fraction.

$$\frac{3(2x-y)}{8} - \frac{x+2y}{8}$$

When you put the fractions over the LCM, 8, remember to replace the fraction bar by a bracket.

$$= \frac{3(2x-y) - (x+2y)}{8}$$

Multiply out the brackets.

$$= \frac{6x - 3y - x - 2y}{8}$$

Collect like terms.

$$= \frac{5x - 5y}{8}$$

**2**  Express $\dfrac{2x+3}{4} - \dfrac{x-1}{3}$ as a single fraction.

$$\frac{2x+3}{4} - \frac{x-1}{3}$$

When you put the fractions over the LCM, 12, remember to replace the fraction bar by a bracket.

$$= \frac{3(2x+3) - 4(x-1)}{12}$$

Multiply out the brackets.

$$= \frac{6x + 9 - 4x + 4}{12}$$

Collect like terms.

$$= \frac{2x + 13}{12}$$

Sometimes the fractions may be written in a different form.

**3**   Simplify $\frac{2}{3}(x+y)-\frac{3}{5}(-x+2y)$.

|  |  |
|---|---|
|  | $\frac{2}{3}(x+y)-\frac{3}{5}(-x+2y)$ |
| Write it in fraction form. The LCM is 15. | $=\dfrac{2(x+y)}{3}-\dfrac{3(-x+2y)}{5}$ |
| When you put the fractions over the LCM, remember to replace the fraction bar by a bracket. | $=\dfrac{10(x+y)-9(-x+2y)}{15}$ |
| Multiply out the brackets. | $=\dfrac{10x+10y+9x-18y}{15}$ |
| Collect like terms. | $=\dfrac{19x-8y}{15}$ |

## Exercise 5

Simplify each of the following expressions.

**1**  $\dfrac{2a-3}{2}+\dfrac{a+4}{2}$

**2**  $\dfrac{3b+4}{3}+\dfrac{2b-6}{3}$

**3**  $\dfrac{4c-3}{5}-\dfrac{2c+1}{5}$

**4**  $\dfrac{7x-14}{10}-\dfrac{2x+1}{10}$

**5**  $\dfrac{z+5}{4}+\dfrac{3z-5}{2}$

**6**  $\dfrac{2n+7}{3}-\dfrac{5n+6}{4}$

**7**  $\dfrac{5u-3}{4}+\dfrac{u-3}{6}$

**8**  $\dfrac{u-v}{6}-\dfrac{u+v}{8}$

**9**  $\dfrac{3a-2}{4}+2a$

**10**  $3b-\dfrac{5b-1}{2}$

**11**  $4x-\dfrac{13x+y}{3}$

**12**  $\dfrac{3c-2d}{10}+\dfrac{2c-3d}{15}$

**13**  $\dfrac{6h+5k}{7}-\dfrac{4h-6k}{21}$

**14**  $\dfrac{4a+6b}{9}+\dfrac{a-4b}{6}$

**15**  $\dfrac{3(a-b)}{2}-\dfrac{4(a+b)}{3}$

**16**  $\dfrac{3(u+2v)}{4}+\dfrac{5(2u-v)}{6}$

**17** $\frac{2}{3}(3m+2n)-\frac{3}{4}(2m-n)$    **18** $\frac{5}{6}(b-3c)+\frac{3}{8}(4b+3c)$

**19** $\dfrac{a+3b-2c}{3}-\dfrac{5a-3b+2c}{6}$    **20** $\dfrac{3u+4v+7}{5}-3v$

**21** $\dfrac{5m-3}{6}-\dfrac{2m-5}{3}+\dfrac{4m+1}{12}$

**22** $\dfrac{3a-b}{2}-\dfrac{2b+c}{4}+\dfrac{2a+4b-9c}{12}$

**23** $x-\frac{1}{3}(x+3)+\frac{1}{5}(x-3)+2$

**24** $\frac{3}{4}(5a-3b)-\dfrac{4a+7b}{5}+\frac{1}{20}(a+3b)$

**25** $\dfrac{3(2m-3n)}{2}-\dfrac{4(3m+n)}{9}-\dfrac{3m-17n}{18}$

# 6    Linear equations

You know how to solve equations of the type $3x = 18$. You divide both sides by 3, to get the solution $x = 6$. To solve more complicated equations the technique is to change them, little by little, into simpler equations until you get them into a form that you recognise. The trick is to make your changes effective, so the equations really do become simpler.

One major aim is to isolate the term or terms involving $x$ so that they are on one side of the equation, and everything else is on the other.

Examine the following examples. Look at what is done at each step to make the new equation simpler.

**1**    Solve the equation $3x + 4 = 25$.

| | |
|---|---|
| | $3x + 4 = 25$ |
| Subtract 4 from both sides. | $3x = 21$ |
| Divide both sides by 3. | $x = 7$ |

It is important to check your answer.

$$3 \times 7 + 4 = 25 \quad ✔$$

**2**    Solve the equation $2x + 2 = 5x - 4$.

| | |
|---|---|
| | $2x + 2 = 5x - 4$ |
| Subtract $5x$ from both sides. | $-3x + 2 = -4$ |
| Subtract 2 from both sides. | $-3x = -6$ |
| Divide both sides by $-3$. | $x = 2$ |
| Now check. | $2 \times 2 + 2 = 6$ and $5 \times 2 - 4 = 6$ ✔ |

Look very carefully at Example 2. If you can get an equation to a form such as $2x + 2 = 5x - 4$ with no fractions or brackets, solving it should be completely routine. If this is true, then you should be trying always to get an equation into this form, and let the routine take over.

In equations where there are fractions, try to eliminate them, usually by multiplying by a suitable number.

In equations with brackets, multiply them out.

The methods which are given are not the only methods you could use. You can often do one or more lines at once.

**3**  Solve the equation $\dfrac{3x}{5} = \dfrac{2}{3}$.

$$\frac{3x}{5} = \frac{2}{3}$$

Multiply both sides by 15 to clear the fractions.

$$15 \times \frac{3x}{5} = 15 \times \frac{2}{3}$$

Cancel the expressions on both sides.

$$9x = 10$$

Divide both sides by 9.

$$x = \frac{10}{9} = 1\tfrac{1}{9}$$

Now check.

$$\frac{3}{5} \times \frac{10}{9} = \frac{2}{3} \quad \checkmark$$

**4**  Solve the equation $\dfrac{x}{0.3} + 3x = 3(x + 2)$.

$$\frac{x}{0.3} + 3x = 3(x + 2)$$

Multiply both sides by 3 to remove the 0.3.

$$3\left(\frac{x}{0.3} + 3x\right) = 3 \times 3(x + 2)$$

Simplify the expressions on both sides.

$$10x + 9x = 9(x + 2)$$

Simplify the expressions on both sides.

$$19x = 9x + 18$$

Subtract $9x$ from each side.

$$10x = 18$$

19

|   |   |
|---|---|
| Divide both sides by 10. | $x = 1.8$ |
| Now check. | $\dfrac{1.8}{0.3} + 3 \times 1.8 = 11.4$ and |
|   | $3(1.8 + 2) = 11.4$ ✔ |

**5** Solve the equation $\dfrac{3x}{2} - \dfrac{x}{3} = \dfrac{5(x-4)}{6}$.

$$\frac{3x}{2} - \frac{x}{3} = \frac{5(x-4)}{6}$$

Multiply both sides by 6 to remove the fractions.

$$6 \times \left(\frac{3x}{2} - \frac{x}{3}\right) = 6 \times \frac{5(x-4)}{6}$$

Simplify the expressions on both sides.

$$9x - 2x = 5(x - 4)$$

Simplify the expressions on both sides.

$$7x = 5x - 20$$

Subtract $5x$ from both sides.

$$2x = -20$$

Divide both sides by 2.

$$x = -10$$

Now check.

$$\frac{3 \times -10}{2} - \frac{-10}{3} = \frac{-90 + 20}{6} = \frac{-70}{6}$$

$$\text{and } \frac{5(-10-4)}{6} = \frac{-70}{6} \ ✔$$

**6** Solve the equation $\dfrac{2x - 11}{3} - \dfrac{x + 5}{6} = 2$.

$$\frac{2x-11}{3} - \frac{x+5}{6} = 2$$

Multiply both sides by 6 to remove the fractions.

$$6 \times \left(\frac{2x-11}{3} - \frac{x+5}{6}\right) = 12$$

Simplify the expressions on both sides.

$$2(2x - 11) - (x + 5) = 12$$

Simplify the expressions on both sides.

$$4x - 22 - x - 5 = 12$$

| Simplify the expressions on both sides. | $3x - 27 = 12$ |
| Add 27 to both sides. | $3x = 39$ |
| Divide both sides by 3. | $x = 13$ |
| Now check. | $\dfrac{2 \times 13 - 11}{3} - \dfrac{13 + 5}{6} = 5 - 3 = 2$ ✔ |

# Exercise 6

Solve the following equations, and check the solutions.

**1**  $7a = 3a + 20$                     **2**  $5b - 12 = 3$

**3**  $7c - 6 = c$                        **4**  $8d - 44 = 0$

**5**  $7 = 9 - 3m$                        **6**  $8 = 4n + 5$

**7**  $20 - 2t = 3t$                      **8**  $1 + 2u = 22 - 5u$

**9**  $5 = 11 - 6v + 9$                   **10**  $2\frac{1}{2}x - 4 = 10 - 3\frac{1}{2}x$

**11**  $3 + 2y - 24 = 14 - 3y$            **12**  $2k = 3k + 4 - 5k$

**13**  $8 - h = 5 - 4h + 3$              **14**  $2a + 20 = 5a + 6$

**15**  $8 + 4d - 7 = 4 - d$              **16**  $2e = 20 - 3e - 9$

**17**  $2x + 19 - 5x = x - 5$            **18**  $12 - 3a - 3 = 9 - 5a$

**19**  $1\frac{1}{2}b - 4\frac{1}{2} = 1\frac{1}{2} + \frac{3}{4}b$   **20**  $a - 10\frac{1}{2} = 10\frac{1}{2} - \frac{2}{5}a$

**21**  $10 + 3x - 7 = 7x + 8 - 6x$       **22**  $7 = 9 + 3x - 5$

**23**  $1 + 3m + 5 = m + 18 - 4m$        **24**  $5n + 7 + 2n = 8 + 3n + 5$

**25**  $\dfrac{x}{2} = \dfrac{x}{3} + \dfrac{1}{2}$   **26**  $\dfrac{a}{2} + \dfrac{1}{4} = \dfrac{a}{4} + \dfrac{3}{2}$

**27**  $\dfrac{3m}{5} - 1 = \dfrac{m}{3} + \dfrac{3}{5}$   **28**  $3y - \dfrac{2}{9} = 4\dfrac{7}{9}$

**29**  $\dfrac{5d}{3} + 1 = \dfrac{d}{6} + 3$   **30**  $\dfrac{9u}{10} - \dfrac{3}{5} = \dfrac{2u}{5} + \dfrac{7}{10}$

**31**  $1.3x - 2.3 = 0.9x - 1.5$         **32**  $1.1a = 0.5a + 0.9$

**33**  $2.03m - 0.5 = 1.98m$             **34**  $3.2n + 0.99 = 3.13n + 1.2$

21

**35** $\dfrac{x-5}{2} = \dfrac{x-3}{4}$

**36** $\dfrac{4t+3}{5} = \dfrac{t+3}{2}$

**37** $\dfrac{2d+7}{6} + \dfrac{d-5}{3} = 0$

**38** $\dfrac{5e-1}{4} - \dfrac{7e+4}{8} = 0$

**39** $\dfrac{7m+2}{3} - \dfrac{9m-2}{5} = 2$

**40** $\dfrac{4n+1}{3} - 1\tfrac{1}{2} = \dfrac{2n+5}{6}$

**41** $\dfrac{4x-3}{2} = \dfrac{9x-6}{8} + 2\tfrac{3}{4}$

**42** $\dfrac{3(2a+1)}{4} - \dfrac{5(a+5)}{6} = 0$

**43** $\tfrac{3}{8}(4u-5) - \tfrac{5}{12}(3u-4) = \tfrac{1}{6}$

**44** $\tfrac{4}{5}(2m+5) = \tfrac{2}{3}(2m+7) - \tfrac{2}{15}$

**45** $\dfrac{6m-3}{7} - \dfrac{2m+1}{3} = 0$

**46** $\dfrac{2a-1}{3} - \dfrac{a+5}{4} = \tfrac{1}{2}$

**47** $\dfrac{7x-1}{4} - \tfrac{1}{2} = \dfrac{4x+2}{3}$

**48** $\dfrac{2(5t-3)}{3} - \dfrac{3(5t-2)}{5} = \dfrac{8}{15}$

**49** $\tfrac{7}{6}(3x-1) - 8\tfrac{1}{3} = \tfrac{3}{2}(2x-5)$

**50** $\dfrac{3a-1}{4} + \dfrac{7a-3}{6} = \dfrac{5a+2}{3}$

**51** $\dfrac{4m}{3} - \dfrac{17}{21} = \dfrac{6m-1}{7}$

**52** $\tfrac{2}{3}(4d-1) - \tfrac{1}{2} = \tfrac{5}{6}(2d+1)$

**53** $\dfrac{n}{5} + 1\tfrac{1}{2}n - \dfrac{11}{20} = \dfrac{5n-1}{4}$

**54** $\dfrac{7b-5}{5} + \dfrac{b-\tfrac{1}{2}}{5} - \dfrac{4b-3}{3} = 0$

# 7   Simultaneous equations

There are two algebraic methods which you should know for solving simultaneous equations: the method of substitution, and the method of elimination. It doesn't matter which you use; choose the one which is simpler for you.

Here is an example of the method of substitution.

**1**   Solve the simultaneous equations $\begin{cases} y = x + 1 \\ x + y = 3 \end{cases}$

$$\begin{cases} y = x + 1 \\ x + y = 3 \end{cases}$$

The technique is to find either $x$ or $y$ from one equation and substitute it into the other.

$$x + (x + 1) = 3$$

Use the technique for linear equations to solve for $x$.

$$x = 1$$

Substitute this value in one of the original equations to find $y$.

$$y = x + 1 = 1 + 1 = 2$$

The solution is
$$x = 1, \ y = 2$$

Now check by substituting in the other original equation.

$$\begin{cases} 2 = 1 + 1 \\ 1 + 2 = 3 \end{cases} ✔$$

It may not always be so easy to make the substitution to start the process.

**2**    Solve the equations $2x + y = 7$, $3x - 2y = 7$.

$$2x + y = 7$$
$$3x - 2y = 7$$

Rewrite one of the equations in the form $y = \ldots$ . In this case, the first is easier.

$$y = 7 - 2x$$

Substitute this value of $y$ in the other equation.

$$3x - 2(7 - 2x) = 7$$

Solve for $x$.

$$x = 3$$

Substitute this value in one of the original equations to find $y$.

$$y = 7 - 2x = 7 - 2 \times 3 = 1$$

Solution: $x = 3$, $y = 1$

Check.

$$3 \times 3 - 2 \times 1 = 7 \quad ✔$$

It is usually only worth using substitution if one of the coefficients in the original equations is 1. If the numbers are bigger, the method of elimination is usually better. This method consists of using multiplication to make the coefficients of one of the unknown letters equal, and then adding the equations or subtracting one equation from the other to eliminate that letter.

**3**    Solve the equations $3x + 2y = 12$, $5x - 3y = 1$.

$$3x + 2y = 12$$
$$5x - 3y = 1$$

Multiply the first equation by 3 and the second by 2. Notice that the coefficients of $y$ in the equations both involve 6.

$$9x + 6y = 36$$
$$10x - 6y = 2$$

Add the equations together.

$$19x = 38$$

Solve this equation.

$$x = 2$$

Substitute this value in one of the original equations to find $y$.

$3 \times 2 + 2y = 12$, leading to $y = 3$

| This gives the final result. | Solution: $x = 2$, $y = 3$ |
|---|---|
| Check. | $5 \times 2 - 3 \times 3 = 1$ ✔ |

You could have solved the previous pair of equations by eliminating $x$ instead of $y$.

**4**  Solve the equations $3x + 2y = 12$, $5x - 3y = 1$.

|  | $3x + 2y = 12$ |
|---|---|
|  | $5x - 3y = 1$ |
| Multiply the first equation by 5 and the second by 3. The coefficients of $x$ in both equations are equal. | $15x + 10y = 60$ |
|  | $15x - 9y = 3$ |
| Subtract the second equation from the first, and solve. | $19y = 57$ leading to |
|  | $y = 3$ |
| Substitute this value in one of the original equations to find $x$. | $3x + 2 \times 3 = 12$, leading to $x = 2$ |
| This gives the final result. | Solution: $x = 2$, $y = 3$ |
| Check. | $5 \times 2 - 3 \times 3 = 1$ ✔ |

If there are fractions or brackets in the original equations, then use suitable multiples to clear the fractions, and multiply out the brackets and proceed as before.

**5**  Solve the equations $\frac{1}{2}x + \frac{1}{3}y = 4$, $\frac{1}{4}y - \frac{1}{3}x = \frac{1}{6}$.

|  | $\frac{1}{2}x + \frac{1}{3}y = 4$ |
|---|---|
|  | $\frac{1}{4}y - \frac{1}{3}x = \frac{1}{6}$ |
| Clear fractions by multiplying one equation by 6 and the other by 12. Rewrite the second equation. | $3x + 2y = 24$ |
|  | $-4x + 3y = 2$ |
| Now solve in the usual way and check the result, as described in earlier examples. These checking steps have been omitted. | Solution: $x = 4$, $y = 6$ |

# *Exercise 7*

Solve the following pairs of simultaneous equations.

**1**   $y = x + 3, \; x + y = 5$      **2**   $y = 2x - 4, 3x + y = 11$

**3**   $2x + y = 0, x + 2y = 3$      **4**   $x + y = 4, 2x - y = 5$

**5**   $y - 2x = 1, 3x - 4y = 1$      **6**   $3x + 2y = 10, 4x - y = 6$

**7**   $x + 2y = 7, \; 3x - 2y = -3$      **8**   $4x - 3y = 1, x - 2y = 4$

**9**   $5x + 2y = 2, 2x + 3y = -8$      **10**   $4x + 3y = 9, 2x + 5y = 15$

**11**   $3x - 2y = 4, 2x + 3y = -6$      **12**   $5y - 2x = 6, 3y - 4x = 12$

**13**   $5x + y = 0, 3x - 2y = 13$      **14**   $5x + y = 7, 2x + 3y = -5$

**15**   $4a = 5b + 5, 2a = 3b + 2$      **16**   $6h = 2k + 9, 3h + 4k = 12$

**17**   $2p - 5q = 8, 3p - 7q = 11$      **18**   $2r + 3s = 29, 3r + 2s = 16$

**19**   $2x + 5y + 1 = 0, 3x + 7y = 1$      **20**   $3a = 2b + 1, 5a = 3b + 3$

**21**   $4x = y + 7, 3x + 4y + 9 = 0$      **22**   $5v = 11 + 3u, 2u + 7v = 3$

**23**   $5d = 2e - 14, 5e = d + 12$      **24**   $6x - 5y = -7, 3x + 4y = 16$

**25**   $3f - 4g = 1, 6f - 6g = 5$      **26**   $4e + 3f = 4, 2e = 5f + 15$

**27**   $4p + 2q + 8 = 0, 6p = 2q - 27$      **28**   $4m = 3n, 8m - 9n = 7$

**29**   $5h + 10k = 28, 15h = 20k - 121$      **30**   $8y + 4z = 7, 6y - 8z = 41$

**31**   $x - \dfrac{y}{2} = 1, \dfrac{x}{2} + \dfrac{y}{3} = 2\tfrac{5}{6}$      **32**   $x + \dfrac{y}{2} = \tfrac{1}{2}, \dfrac{x}{2} - \dfrac{y}{6} = 1\tfrac{1}{2}$

**33**   $3(x + y) = 7(y - x), 5(3x - y) = x + 3$

**34**   $7(a + b) = b - a, 4(3a + 2b) = b - 8$

**35**   $f - 2g + 3 = 2f - 3g + 2 = 1$

**36**   $1.5x - 0.7y = 0.1, 0.3x + 1.1y = 2.5$

**37**   $2.3m + 1.8n = 5.1, 0.9m + 2.4n = 0.3$

**38**   $\dfrac{5x}{8} - \dfrac{y}{2} = \dfrac{1}{4}, \dfrac{2x}{3} - \dfrac{3y}{5} = \dfrac{2}{15}$

**39**   $\dfrac{1}{3}(m - 3n) = 2, \dfrac{m + n}{4} = \dfrac{1}{2}$

**40**   $3(3f + 2g) = 5 - f, 4g + 5 = 2(g - 5f)$

# 8 Expanding brackets

When you remove the brackets from an expression like $(a+b)(c+d)$, each term in the first bracket must multiply each term in the second bracket.

To see why this is true, for the moment give $(c+d)$ the name $X$, and follow the working in Example 1.

**1** Remove the brackets from $(a+b)(c+d)$.

|  | $(a+b)(c+d)$ |
|---|---|
| Let $X=(c+d)$. | $=(a+b)X$ |
| Multiply out the bracket. | $=aX+bX$ |
| But $X=(c+d)$. | $=a(c+d)+b(c+d)$ |
| Multiply the brackets. | $=ac+bc+ad+bd$ |

The working in Example 1 gives the justification for the statement in the first paragraph. You will usually shorten the work as in Example 2.

**2** Remove the brackets from $(a+b)(c+d)$.

|  | $(a+b)(c+d)$ |
|---|---|
| Expand the first bracket. | $=a(c+d)+b(c+d)$ |
| And the second bracket. | $=ac+bc+ad+bd$ |

This process of removing brackets is called expanding the brackets.

**3** Expand $(2x-1)(3x+2)$.

|  | $(2x-1)(3x+2)$ |
|---|---|
| Expand the first bracket. | $=2x(3x+2)-1(3x+2)$ |
| And the second bracket. | $=6x^2+4x-3x-2$ |
| Simplify if possible. | $=6x^2+x-2$ |

**4**   Expand $(2a+3b)(3a-4b)$.

|  | $(2a+3b)(3a-4b)$ |
|---|---|
| Expand the first bracket. | $= 2a(3a-4b)+3b(3a-4b)$ |
| And the second bracket. | $= 6a^2-8ab+9ba-12b^2$ |
| Simplify if possible. | $= 6a^2+ab-12b^2$ |

**5**   Expand $(2x-1)^2$.

|  | $(2x-1)^2$ |
|---|---|
| Rewrite in full as the product of brackets. | $= (2x-1)(2x-1)$ |
| Expand the first bracket. | $= 2x(2x-1)-1(2x-1)$ |
| And the second bracket. | $= 4x^2-2x-2x+1$ |
| Simplify if possible. | $= 4x^2-4x+1$ |

## *Exercise 8*

Expand each of the following.

**1**  $(a-c)(b-d)$   **2**  $(x+y)(p-q)$   **3**  $(a-2b)(c+2d)$

**4**  $(2x-y)(p+2q)$   **5**  $(2h-3k)(h-k)$   **6**  $(a-c)(b-c)$

**7**  $(a+3)(a+4)$   **8**  $(b+2)(b+5)$   **9**  $(m+3)(m-2)$

**10**  $(n-7)(n+2)$   **11**  $(x+2)^2$   **12**  $(y+1)(y-4)$

**13**  $(c-2)(c+5)$   **14**  $(d-3)(d-4)$   **15**  $(p-2)(p-5)$

**16**  $(x-4)^2$   **17**  $(y+1)(y+7)$   **18**  $(a-4)(a+6)$

**19**  $(b-3)(b-7)$   **20**  $(c+5)(c-1)$   **21**  $(3+d)(2+d)$

**22**  $(5-x)(2+x)$   **23**  $(3-y)(4-y)$   **24**  $(m+2n)(m+3n)$

**25**  $(a-3b)(a+2b)$   **26**  $(x-4y)(x-3y)$   **27**  $(p+2q)^2$

**28**  $(m+5n)(m-3n)$   **29**  $(a+5)(2a-3)$

**30**  $(3x+4)(x-2)$   **31**  $(2h-k)(3h+2k)$   **32**  $(5x+2y)(3x+4y)$

**33**  $(3a-2b)^2$   **34**  $(5h+k)^2$   **35**  $(5a-2b)(2a-3b)$

# 9 Factorising

You know how to expand brackets. There are times when you need to carry out the process in the other direction. This is called factorising. The final result must be a product of a number of terms or brackets.

The first type is when there is a factor which multiplies all terms.

**1** Find the factors of $2x + 4y$.

$$2x + 4y$$

2 is a factor of both terms.

$$= 2(x + 2y)$$

**2** Find the factors of $ax + 2ay - 4az$.

$$ax + 2ay - 4az$$

$a$ is a factor of all three terms.

$$= a(x + 2y - 4z)$$

**3** Find the factors of $2a - a(7 - x)$.

$$2a - a(7 - x)$$

$a$ is a factor of both terms.

$$= a[2 - (7 - x)]$$

Simplify the square bracket.

$$= a(-5 + x)$$

The second type results in factors such as $(a + b)(c + d)$.

**4** Find the factors of $ap - 2bq + aq - 2bp$.

$$ap - 2bq + aq - 2bp$$

Group the terms in pairs, so that each pair has a common factor.

$$= (ap - 2bp) + (aq - 2bq)$$

Take out the factors $p$ and $q$.

$$= p(a - 2b) + q(a - 2b)$$

Then, provided that the terms in brackets are identical, you can complete the factorisation.

$$= (p + q)(a - 2b)$$

It is very important that the factors in brackets which appear in the middle step must be the same in order to continue. In the previous case the factor is $(a-2b)$.

**5**  Find the factors of $x^2 - 2xy - 2zy + xz$.

$$x^2 - 2xy - 2zy + xz$$

Group the terms in pairs, so that each pair has a common factor.
$$= (x^2 - 2xy) + (-2zy + xz)$$

Take out the factor in each pair.
$$= x(x-2y) + z(x-2y)$$

Then, as $(x-2y)$ in both parts of the expression, you can complete the factorisation.
$$= (x+z)(x-2y)$$

**6**  Find the factors of $a^2 - bc + ab + ac$.

$$a^2 - bc + ab + ac$$

Group the terms in pairs, so that each pair has a common factor.
$$= (a^2 + ab) + (ac - bc)$$

Take out the factor in each pair.
$$= a(a+b) + c(a-b)$$

Then, as the brackets in both parts of the expression are not the same, you cannot continue.

There are no factors.

You will also need to find the factors of expressions such as $x^2 - 5x + 6$. That is, you will need to be able to write $x^2 - 5x + 6$ in the form $x^2 - 5x + 6 = (x-2)(x-3)$. Carrying out this process is rather like doing a puzzle. You need to look at all the evidence available, and come to a conclusion. You should also realise that it isn't always possible to find factors of expressions like $x^2 - 5x + 6$: for example, there are no factors of $x^2 + 2x + 2$.

**7**  Find the factors of $x^2 + 6x + 5$.

> The term in $x^2$ must arise from brackets of the form $(x......)(x......)$.
> All the signs in $x^2 + 6x + 5$ are positive, so the brackets must be of the form $(x+...)(x+...)$.
> The only factors of 5 are 1 and 5, so if there are factors they must be $(x+1)(x+5)$.
> Check by ~~multiplying~~ out that $(x+1)(x+5)$ is correct.
> Then $x^2 + 6x + 5 = (x+1)(x+5)$.

**8**  Find the factors of $x^2 - 6x + 8$.

> The term in $x^2$ arises from the brackets $(x......)(x......)$.
> The arrangement of signs shows that the brackets are of the form $(x-...)(x-...)$.
> The factors of 8 are 8 and 1, or 4 and 2. This suggests that there are two possibilities, $(x-8)(x-1)$ and $(x-4)(x-2)$.
> Checking shows that $x^2 - 6x + 8 = (x-4)(x-2)$.

**9**  Find the factors of $x^2 - x - 6$.

> The term in $x^2$ arises from the brackets $(x......)(x......)$.
> The constant term, $-6$, is negative, so the brackets must be of the form $(x-...)(x+...)$.
> The factors of 6 are 6 and 1, or 3 and 2. This suggests that there are four possibilities, $(x-6)(x+1)$, $(x+6)(x-1)$, $(x-3)(x+2)$ and $(x+3)(x-2)$.
> Checking these possibilities one by one shows that $x^2 - x - 6 = (x-3)(x+2)$.

When the expression to be factorised is more complicated, the principle is the same, but you have more possibilities to consider. With practice, you can discard some of the possibilities quite quickly.

**1 0** Find the factors of $6x^2 - 5x - 6$.

Looking at the multiple of $x^2$, the signs and the constant term suggests the following possibilities.
The first terms in each bracket must be $(6x\ldots\ldots)(x\ldots\ldots)$ or $(3x\ldots\ldots)(x\ldots\ldots)$.
One of the signs is positive and one is negative.
To get the final 6, the last terms must be one or other of the forms $(\ldots\ldots 6)(\ldots\ldots 1)$ and $(\ldots\ldots 3)(\ldots\ldots 2)$.
Checking shows that $6x^2 - 5x - 6 = (2x - 3)(3x + 2)$.

**1 1** Find the factors of $x^2 + 2x + 2$.

The only possibility is $x^2 + 2x + 2 = (x + 1)(x + 2)$. Checking shows it doesn't work. There are no factors of $x^2 + 2x + 2$.

The example which follows is an important special case. It is called the difference of two squares.

**1 2** Find the factors of $x^2 - 9$.

Checking possibilities shows that $x^2 - 9 = (x - 3)(x + 3)$.

In general, the form $x^2 - y^2 = (x - y)(x + y)$, where $x$ and $y$ can themselves be algebraic expressions, is very useful.

**1 3** Find the factors of $x^2 - (2x + 1)^2$.

|  |  |
|---|---|
|  | $x^2 - (2x + 1)^2$ |
| Use the difference of two squares. | $= \{x + (2x + 1)\}\{x - (2x + 1)\}$ |
| Simplify each bracket. | $= \{3x + 1\}\{-x - 1\}$ |

# *Exercise 9*

Factorise each of the following expressions.

| | | | |
|---|---|---|---|
| **1** | $3x - 6y$ | **2** | $p^2 + 2p$ |
| **3** | $pq - rq$ | **4** | $2a - ab$ |
| **5** | $2c + 4c^2$ | **6** | $ap + bp$ |
| **7** | $3m + m(u - v)$ | **8** | $2a - a(3x + y)$ |
| **9** | $x(3 - a) + bx$ | **10** | $(4m - 3n)p - 5p$ |
| **11** | $a(m + 1) + b(m + 1)$ | **12** | $a(n + 2) - b(n + 2)$ |
| **13** | $ax - x(b - 4c)$ | **14** | $5x(a - b) - 2y(a - b)$ |
| **15** | $3h(5u - v) + 2k(5u - v)$ | **16** | $m(u - v) + m^2$ |
| **17** | $d(3h + k) - 4d^2$ | **18** | $5a^2 + a(b - c)$ |

Factorise each of the following expressions, where possible.

| | | | |
|---|---|---|---|
| **19** | $mx + nx + my + ny$ | **20** | $hu + hv - ku - kv$ |
| **21** | $am + 2bm + 2bn + an$ | **22** | $2ce + 2df - de - 4cf$ |
| **23** | $am - an + m - n$ | **24** | $a^3 + a^2 + a + 1$ |
| **25** | $3sx - 5ty + 5tx - 3sy$ | **26** | $hk - 2km + 3hn - 6mn$ |
| **27** | $2gk - 3gl + 2hk - 3hl$ | **28** | $3ce + 4df - 2de - 6cf$ |
| **29** | $a^2 + 8a + 15$ | **30** | $b^2 - 7b + 10$ |
| **31** | $c^2 + 4c - 21$ | **32** | $d^2 - 5d - 14$ |
| **33** | $e^2 + 2e - 8$ | **34** | $w^2 + 5w + 6$ |
| **35** | $x^2 + 5x - 6$ | **36** | $y^2 - 5y + 6$ |
| **37** | $z^2 - 5z - 6$ | **38** | $2d^2 + 3d + 1$ |
| **39** | $2e^2 - 3e + 1$ | **40** | $2f^2 - f - 1$ |
| **41** | $x^2 - 4$ | **42** | $x^2 + 4x + 5$ |
| **43** | $4x^2 - 9$ | **44** | $a^2 + 7a + 10$ |
| **45** | $a^2 + 7ab + 10b^2$ | **46** | $a^2b^2 + 7ab + 10$ |
| **47** | $x^2 - 2xy - 15y^2$ | **48** | $m^2 + 10m - 24$ |
| **49** | $n^2 - 10n - 24$ | **50** | $v^2 - 11v + 24$ |
| **51** | $m^2 + 4m - 21$ | **52** | $m^2 + 4mn - 21n^2$ |
| **53** | $m^2n^2 + 4mn - 21$ | **54** | $3a^2 - 4a + 1$ |
| **55** | $3b^2 + b - 2$ | **56** | $3c^2 + c + 2$ |
| **57** | $x^2 - 1$ | **58** | $1 - y^2$ |
| **59** | $9 - 4c^2$ | **60** | $25k^2 - 16$ |
| **61** | $3 - 3x^2$ | **62** | $81 - w^2$ |
| **63** | $81 + w^2$ | | |

# 10 Changing the subject of a formula

Changing the subject of a formula is about solving equations which contain letters; this is very similar to solving equations with numbers. The technique is to change them, little by little, into simpler equations until you get them into a form that you recognise and can solve.

As with ordinary equations, the aim is to isolate the term or terms involving $x$ so that they are on one side of the equation, and everything else is on the other.

Work through the following examples. Look in particular at what is done at each step to make what follows simpler.

**1**   Solve for $x$ the equation $a + x = b$.

$$a + x = b$$

Subtract $a$ from both sides to isolate $x$.

$$x = b - a$$

**2**   Solve for $x$ the equation $cx = d$.

$$cx = d$$

Divide both sides by $c$.

$$x = \frac{d}{c}$$

**3**   Solve for $x$ the equation $ax + b = cx$.

$$ax + b = cx$$

Subtract $ax$ from both sides to begin the process of isolating $x$.

$$b = cx - ax$$

Find the multiple of $x$ on the right-hand side. This will often involve a factorisation.

$$b = x(c - a)$$

Divide both sides by this multiple.

$$x = \frac{b}{c - a}$$

Example 3 shows an important new feature, which doesn't arise in ordinary equations. When the equation is in the form $b = cx - ax$ with the $x$'s isolated on one side, you need to factorise to find the multiple of $x$ on that side. Then you can divide by it.

Example 4 shows the same feature.

**4**    Solve for $x$ the equation $ax + b = cx + d$.

$$ax + b = cx + d$$

Subtract $b$ from both sides to begin isolating $x$.
$$ax = cx + d - b$$

Subtract $cx$ from both sides to complete the isolation of $x$.
$$ax - cx = d - b$$

Factorise to find the multiple of $x$ on the left-hand side.
$$x(a - c) = d - b$$

Divide both sides by this multiple, $(a - c)$.
$$x = \frac{d - b}{(a - c)}$$

Solving equations of the form $ax + b = cx + d$, without fractions and brackets, should become routine. Once you can solve this type of equation, you should aim with more complex equations, to get them into this form.

When the equations are more complicated, you may need to multiply by something to remove fractions, remove brackets, square to remove square roots and so on. But always have the aim to get to the form $ax + b = cx + d$ which you know you can solve.

**5** Solve for $x$ the equation $\dfrac{a}{x} + 2 = b$.

$$\frac{a}{x} + 2 = b$$

Multiply both sides by $x$ to remove the fraction.

$$x\left(\frac{a}{x} + 2\right) = bx$$

Simplify the expressions on each side.

$$a + 2x = bx$$

Subtract $2x$ from both sides to begin isolating $x$.

$$a = bx - 2x$$

Find the multiple of $x$ on the right-hand side.

$$a = x(b - 2)$$

Divide both sides by this multiple, $(b - 2)$.

$$x = \frac{a}{b - 2}$$

**6** Solve for $x$ the equation $\dfrac{a}{b + x} + c = d$.

$$\frac{a}{b + x} + c = d$$

Multiply both sides by $(b + x)$ to remove the fractions.

$$(b + x) \times \left(\frac{a}{b + x} + c\right) = (b + x)d$$

Simplify the expressions on each side.

$$a + (b + x)c = bd + xd$$

Simplify the expressions on each side.

$$a + bc + xc = bd + xd$$

Subtract $xc$ from both sides to begin isolating $x$.

$$a + bc = bd + xd - xc$$

Subtract $bd$ from both sides to complete isolating $x$ on the right.

$$a + bc - bd = xd - xc$$

Find the multiple of $x$ on the right-hand side.

$$a + bc - bd = x(d - c)$$

|  |  |
|---|---|
| Divide both sides by this multiple, $(d-c)$. | $$x = \frac{a+bc-bd}{d-c}$$ |

When there are square roots involved, you may need to square the original equation.

**7** Solve for $x$ the equation $\sqrt{a-x} = b$.

|  |  |
|---|---|
|  | $$\sqrt{a-x} = b$$ |
| Square both sides to remove the square root sign. | $$a - x = b^2$$ |
| Add $x$ to both sides. | $$a = b^2 + x$$ |
| Subtract $b^2$ from both sides to complete isolating $x$ on the right. | $$a - b^2 = x$$ |

In the following example, it is better to delay the squaring process.

**8** Solve for $x$ the equation $\sqrt{a} - \sqrt{x} = b$.

|  |  |
|---|---|
|  | $$\sqrt{a} - \sqrt{x} = b$$ |
| This equation is slightly different. Notice that you can isolate $\sqrt{x}$ by adding $\sqrt{x}$ to both sides. | $$\sqrt{a} = b + \sqrt{x}$$ |
| Subtract $b$ from both sides. | $$\sqrt{a} - b = \sqrt{x}$$ |
| Square both sides. | $$x = \left(\sqrt{a} - b\right)^2$$ |

**9** Solve for $x$ the equation $\dfrac{x}{x-a}+\dfrac{b}{x-b}=1$.

$$\frac{x}{x-a}+\frac{b}{x-b}=1$$

| | |
|---|---|
| Multiply by $(x-a)(x-b)$ to clear the fractions. | $x(x-b)+b(x-a)$ <br> $\quad=(x-a)(x-b)$ |
| Simplify the expressions on both sides. | $x^2-bx+bx-ab$ <br> $\quad=x^2-ax-bx+ab$ |
| Subtract $x^2$ from both sides. | $-bx+bx-ab$ <br> $\quad=-ax-bx+ab$ |
| Simplify the expressions on both sides. | $-ab=-ax-bx+ab$ |
| Subtract $ab$ from both sides. | $-2ab=-ax-bx$ |
| Find the multiple of $x$ on the right-hand side. | $-2ab=-x(a+b)$ |
| Divide both sides by this multiple. | $x=\dfrac{2ab}{a+b}$ |

**10** Solve for $x$ the equation $\sqrt{x^2-a^2}=a$.

$$\sqrt{x^2-a^2}=a$$

| | |
|---|---|
| Square both sides. | $x^2-a^2=a^2$ |
| Subtract $a^2$ from both sides. | $x^2=2a^2$ |
| Take the square root of both sides, remembering to include the negative square root. | $x=\pm a\sqrt{2}$ |

# *Exercise 10*

Solve for $x$ the following equations.

**1**   $x + a = b$      **2**   $a - x = b$      **3**   $ax = b$

**4**   $ax + bx = c$      **5**   $ax + b = x$      **6**   $\dfrac{a}{x} = b$

**7**   $\dfrac{a}{x} + b = c$      **8**   $\dfrac{x}{a} + b = c$      **9**   $\dfrac{x}{a} + \dfrac{x}{b} = 1$

**10**   $\dfrac{a}{x} + \dfrac{b}{x} = 1$      **11**   $a(x + b) = c$      **12**   $ax = b(c + x)$

**13**   $a(b - x) = cx$      **14**   $\dfrac{x}{2a} + \dfrac{x}{3a} = b$      **15**   $x(a - b) = b(c - x)$

**16**   $\dfrac{a}{b - x} = c$      **17**   $a = \dfrac{2b + 3x}{3b - 2x}$      **18**   $\sqrt{x} = a$

**19**   $\sqrt{(2x)} = a$      **20**   $2\sqrt{x} = a$      **21**   $\sqrt{\dfrac{x}{2}} = a$

**22**   $\dfrac{\sqrt{x}}{2} = a$      **23**   $a\sqrt{x} = b$      **24**   $\sqrt{(ax)} = b$

**25**   $\sqrt[3]{\dfrac{x}{a}} = b$      **26**   $x^2 = a^4$      **27**   $x^2 = a$

**28**   $\sqrt{x + a} = b$      **29**   $\sqrt{x} + a = b$      **30**   $\sqrt{x^2 + a^2} = b$

**31**   $\sqrt{x^2 + a^2} = 3a$            **32**   $\dfrac{a}{x} - 1 = \dfrac{b}{2x}$

**33**   $a\sqrt{(x - 1)} = b$           **34**   $a\sqrt{x} - 1 = b$

**35**   $(ax - b)(bx + a) = (bx^2 + a)a$    **36**   $\dfrac{a}{a - x} = \dfrac{b}{b + x}$

**37**   $\dfrac{a}{b - x} = \dfrac{b}{a + x}$        **38**   $a(a^2 - x) = b(b^2 - x)$

**39**   $\dfrac{x}{x + a} - \dfrac{a}{x + b} = 1$      **40**   $\dfrac{x^2}{a^2} + \dfrac{y^2}{b^2} = 1$

**41**   $\sqrt{a^2 + bx} = a + b$      **42**   $\sqrt{b^2 + 2ax} = x + a$

**43**   $2\sqrt{x^2 + b^2} = 2x + b$     **44**   $\sqrt{x^2 - a^2} + a = x$

**45**   $\sqrt{x^2 - a^2} - x = a$       **46**   $\dfrac{x + a}{a} - \dfrac{x - b}{b} = \dfrac{x}{b}$

**47** $\dfrac{x-a}{x-b} - \dfrac{x}{x-b} = \dfrac{a}{x}$

**48** $\dfrac{1}{x+a} = \dfrac{2}{x+b} - \dfrac{1}{x-a}$

**49** $\dfrac{2}{x} - \dfrac{1}{x+a} = \dfrac{2}{2x-a}$

**50** $x = a + \sqrt{b(x-a)}$

In each of the following questions, solve the equation for the letter printed in bold faced type after each question. If there are two letters, solve for each in turn.

**51** $P = \dfrac{N+2}{D}$    **N**

**52** $k = \dfrac{brt}{v-b}$    **b**

**53** $C = 2\pi r$    **r**

**54** $P = aW + b$    **W**

**55** $s = \dfrac{n}{2}(a+l)$    **n**, **l**

**56** $A = P + \dfrac{PRT}{100}$    **P** , **T**

**57** $S = 2\pi r(r+h)$    **h**

**58** $v^2 = u^2 + 2as$    **s** , **u**

**59** $L = \dfrac{Wh}{a(W+P)}$    **W**

**60** $\dfrac{L}{E} = \dfrac{2a}{R-r}$    **R**

**61** $R = \sqrt{\dfrac{ax-P}{Q+bx}}$    **x**

**62** $D = \sqrt{\dfrac{3h}{2}}$    **h**

**63** $S = 4\pi r^2$    **r**

**64** $T = 2\pi\sqrt{\dfrac{I}{MH}}$    **M**

**65** $A = \tfrac{1}{2}m(v^2 - u^2)$    **u**

**66** $d = a\sqrt[3]{\dfrac{H}{N}}$    **H**

**67** $M = \dfrac{wd}{4}\left(l - \dfrac{d}{2}\right)$    **l**

**68** $S = \dfrac{wd}{l}\left(l - \dfrac{d}{2}\right)$    **l**

**69** $H = \dfrac{(T-t)\pi Rn}{275}$    **t**

**70** $H = \dfrac{w^2}{2g}(R^2 - r^2)$    **r**

**71** $T = \sqrt{\dfrac{Pbh}{4+a^2}}$    **b**, **a**

**72** $x = \dfrac{a+2b}{3(a+b)}h$    **a**

**73** $v = w\sqrt{a^2 - x^2}$    **x**

**74** $A = \pi r\sqrt{h^2 + r^2}$    **h**

**75** $T = \sqrt{H + \dfrac{w^2 l^2}{4}}$    **H** , **l**

**76** $\dfrac{1}{u} + \dfrac{1}{v} = \dfrac{2}{f}$    **u**

**77** $V = \dfrac{1}{3}\sqrt{\dfrac{s^3}{8\pi}}$    **s**

**78** $A = \sqrt{\dfrac{P^2 - 2Q^2}{2P^2 + Q^2}}$    **P**

**79** $A = \pi r\sqrt{h^2 + r^2} + \pi r^2$    **h**

**80** $r = \dfrac{f}{2} + \sqrt{\dfrac{f^2}{4} + q^2}$    **q**

# 11   Quadratic equations (1)

An equation such as $x^2 - 4x + 3 = 0$, which has terms in $x^2$, $x$ and a constant term is called a quadratic equation.

This chapter gives practice on solving equations using a technique based on factorising. The next chapter shows a second method.

The important step in this method is to notice that if two numbers multiply together to give 0, one of the numbers must be 0. Notice how this is used in the examples which follow.

**1**   Solve the equation $x^2 - 4x + 3 = 0$.

|  |  |
|---|---|
|  | $x^2 - 4x + 3 = 0$ |
| Factorise the expression, if you can. | $(x-1)(x-3) = 0$ |
| Two numbers multiply to give 0, so one of them must be 0. | Either $(x-1) = 0$ or $(x-3) = 0$ |
| Then solve these equations. | $x = 1$ or $x = 3$ |

**2**   Solve the equation $2x^2 - 5x + 2 = 0$.

|  |  |
|---|---|
|  | $2x^2 - 5x + 2 = 0$ |
| Factorise the expression, if you can. | $(2x-1)(x-2) = 0$ |
| Two numbers multiply to give 0, so one of them must be 0. | Either $(2x-1) = 0$ or $(x-2) = 0$ |
| Then solve these equations. | $x = \frac{1}{2}$ or $x = 2$ |

Notice that the expression may not have factors. Or, it may have factors, but you cannot find them. In either of these situations, use the formula given in the next chapter.

# *Exercise 11*

Solve each of the following quadratic equations using factorisation.

| | | | |
|---|---|---|---|
| **1** | $a^2 - 3a + 2 = 0$ | **2** | $b^2 + 5b + 6 = 0$ |
| **3** | $c^2 - c - 2 = 0$ | **4** | $d^2 + 2d - 3 = 0$ |
| **5** | $e^2 - 7e + 10 = 0$ | **6** | $m^2 - 4m = 0$ |
| **7** | $n^2 + 5n = 0$ | **8** | $p^2 + 7p + 12 = 0$ |
| **9** | $q^2 + 2q - 8 = 0$ | **10** | $x^2 - 2x + 1 = 0$ |
| **11** | $y^2 - 5y + 4 = 0$ | **12** | $a^2 - 9a = 0$ |
| **13** | $b^2 - 9 = 0$ | **14** | $c^2 = 25$ |
| **15** | $u^2 - 8u - 9 = 0$ | **16** | $v^2 + 2v - 35 = 0$ |
| **17** | $x^2 - 6x + 9 = 0$ | **18** | $y^2 + 8y + 16 = 0$ |
| **19** | $z^2 - 4z = 0$ | **20** | $z^2 - 4 = 0$ |
| **21** | $h^2 - 15h + 54 = 0$ | **22** | $h^2 - 15h - 54 = 0$ |
| **23** | $2m^2 - 5m = 0$ | **24** | $2m^2 - 5m + 3 = 0$ |
| **25** | $2m^2 - 5m - 3 = 0$ | **26** | $3n^2 + n = 0$ |
| **27** | $a^2 + a = 90$ | **28** | $b^2 - b = 72$ |
| **29** | $3x^2 + 4x + 1 = 0$ | **30** | $9h^2 = 6h - 1$ |
| **31** | $16k^2 + 8k + 1 = 0$ | **32** | $2c^2 + 5c + 3 = 0$ |
| **33** | $3d^2 - 5d - 2 = 0$ | **34** | $4e^2 - 20e + 25 = 0$ |
| **35** | $9f^2 + 12f + 4 = 0$ | **36** | $4a^2 - 11a = 3$ |
| **37** | $b^2 + 7b = 44$ | **38** | $7m^2 = 3m$ |
| **39** | $5n^2 + 2n = 0$ | **40** | $2p^2 - 11p + 5 = 0$ |
| **41** | $5q^2 + 11q + 2 = 0$ | **42** | $25z^2 = 9$ |
| **43** | $6y^2 = y + 1$ | **44** | $6h^2 + 13h - 5 = 0$ |
| **45** | $16t^2 = 49$ | **46** | $6h^2 + 13h - 5 = 0$ |
| **47** | $8s^2 + 14s = 15$ | **48** | $6x^2 = 7x + 20$ |
| **49** | $12y^2 + y - 35 = 0$ | **50** | $63z = 49 + 18z^2$ |

# 12    Quadratic equations (2)

Completing the square is a technique which forms the basis for getting the well-known formula for solving quadratic equations.

Completing the square involves expressions such as $x^2 + 6x$ and $x^2 - 8x$. What number do you add to $x^2 + 6x$ to make it into a form $(x + a)^2$, where $a$ is a number you must find? What number do you add to $x^2 - 8x$ to make it into a form $(x + b)^2$, where $b$ is a number you must find?

The answer, which you should learn, comes from looking at the coefficient of $x$. Halve it, and that is the value you want for $a$. But beware: this rule works only for expressions starting $x^2$. It doesn't work for expressions starting $2x^2$ or $3x^2$.

**1**    What number do you add to $x^2 + 8x$ to make it into a perfect square?

|  |  |
|---|---|
|  | $x^2 + 8x$ |
| Find the coefficient of $x$, and halve it, giving 4. | $x^2 + 8x + 16 = (x + 4)^2$ |
|  | The number added is 16. |

**2**    The expression $x^2 - 9x + k$ is a perfect square of the form $(x + a)^2$. Find $k$, and find $a$.

|  |  |
|---|---|
|  | $x^2 - 9x + k$ |
| Find the coefficient of $x$, and halve it, giving $-4\frac{1}{2}$. | $x^2 - 9x + \left(4\frac{1}{2}\right)^2 = \left(x - 4\frac{1}{2}\right)^2$ |
| This leads to the values of $k$ and $a$. | $k = \left(4\frac{1}{2}\right)^2 = 20\frac{1}{4}$;  $a = -4\frac{1}{2}$ |

Completing the square can enable you to solve quadratic equations.

**3**  Solve the quadratic equation $x^2 - 8x + 3 = 0$.

$$x^2 - 8x + 3 = 0$$

Subtract 3 from both sides.

$$x^2 - 8x \qquad = -3.$$

Completing the square on the left-hand side requires 16 to be added, so add 16 to both sides.

$$x^2 - 8x + 16 = 13$$

Rewrite the left-hand side.

$$(x - 4)^2 = 13$$

Square root both sides, remembering the ± sign.

$$(x - 4) = \pm\sqrt{13}$$

Add 4 to both sides.

$$x = 4 \pm \sqrt{13}$$

Sometimes you need to make an additional step if the coefficient of $x^2$ is not equal to 1.

**4**  Solve the quadratic equation $2x^2 - 14x + 9 = 0$.

$$2x^2 - 14x + 9 = 0$$

Divide by 2 to make the coefficient of $x^2$ equal to 1.

$$x^2 - 7x + 4\tfrac{1}{2} = 0$$

Subtract $4\tfrac{1}{2}$ from both sides.

$$x^2 - 7x = -4\tfrac{1}{2}.$$

Add $\left(3\tfrac{1}{2}\right)^2 = 12\tfrac{1}{4}$ to both sides to complete the square.

$$x^2 - 7x + 12\tfrac{1}{4} = 7\tfrac{3}{4}$$

Rewrite the left-hand side.

$$\left(x - 3\tfrac{1}{2}\right)^2 = 7\tfrac{3}{4}$$

Square root both sides, remembering the ± sign.

$$\left(x - 3\tfrac{1}{2}\right) = \pm\sqrt{7\tfrac{3}{4}}$$

Add $3\tfrac{1}{2}$ to both sides.

$$x = 3\tfrac{1}{2} \pm \sqrt{7\tfrac{3}{4}}$$

**5** Solve the quadratic equation $ax^2 + bx + c = 0$.

$$ax^2 + bx + c = 0$$

Divide by $a$ to make the coefficient of $x^2$ equal to 1.

$$x^2 + \frac{b}{a}x + \frac{c}{a} = 0$$

Subtract $\dfrac{c}{a}$ from both sides.

$$x^2 + \frac{b}{a}x = -\frac{c}{a}.$$

Add $\left(\dfrac{b}{2a}\right)^2 = \dfrac{b^2}{4a^2}$ to both sides to complete the square.

$$x^2 + \frac{b}{a}x + \frac{b^2}{4a^2} = \frac{b^2}{4a^2} - \frac{c}{a}$$

Rewrite the left-hand side, and express the right-hand side as a single fraction.

$$\left(x + \frac{b}{2a}\right)^2 = \frac{b^2 - 4ac}{4a^2}$$

Square root both sides, remembering the $\pm$ sign.

$$\left(x + \frac{b}{2a}\right) = \pm\frac{\sqrt{b^2 - 4ac}}{\sqrt{4a^2}}$$

Simplify the denominator on the right-hand side.

$$\left(x + \frac{b}{2a}\right) = \pm\frac{\sqrt{b^2 - 4ac}}{2a}$$

Subtract $\dfrac{b}{2a}$ from both sides.

$$x = \frac{-b}{2a} \pm \frac{\sqrt{b^2 - 4ac}}{2a}$$

Re-organise the right-hand side.

$$x = \frac{-b \pm \sqrt{b^2 - 4ac}}{2a}$$

**6** Use the quadratic equation formula to solve the equation $2x^2 - 5x - 4 = 0$.

$$2x^2 - 5x - 4 = 0$$

Compare the equation $ax^2 + bx + c = 0$ with the equation $2x^2 - 5x - 4 = 0$.

Put $a = 2$, $b = -5$ and $c = -4$.

Substitute these values of $a$, $b$ and $c$ into the formula

$$x = \frac{-b \pm \sqrt{b^2 - 4ac}}{2a}.$$

Simplify the right-hand side.

Simplify the right-hand side.

The solutions are

$$x = \frac{-(-5) \pm \sqrt{(-5)^2 - 4.2.(-4)}}{2 \times 2}$$

$$x = \frac{5 \pm \sqrt{25 + 32}}{4}$$

$$x = \frac{5 \pm \sqrt{57}}{4}$$

Completing the square can also be useful for finding the greatest or smallest value of a quadratic expression.

**7**  Find the minimum value of $x^2 - 6x + 3$.

Completing the square enables you to write $x^2 - 6x + 3$ in the following form.

$$\left(x^2 - 6x + 9\right) - 6 =$$

$$(x - 3)^2 - 6$$

Looking at the right-hand side, the minimum value of the perfect square is 0, so the smallest value of the expression is $-6$.

The minimum value of the $x^2 - 6x + 3$ is $-6$.

**8**  Find the maximum value of $3 + 8x - x^2$.

Completing the square relies on $x^2$ having a coefficient of 1, so re-write in this form.

$$3 + 8x - x^2 = 3 - \left(x^2 - 8x\right)$$

Complete the square with 16, and then adjust so the expression stays the same.

$$3 - \left(x^2 - 8x\right) =$$

$$19 - \left(x^2 - 8x + 16\right)$$

Re-write the right-hand side.

$$19 - (x - 4)^2$$

Looking at the right-hand side, the maximum value of the expression is 19.

The maximum value of the $19 - (x - 4)^2$ is 19.

# Exercise 12

In each of questions **1** to **24**, add the term which will make the given expression into a perfect square. Then write the result as the square of an expression in a bracket.

**1**    $a^2 + 8a$       **2**    $b^2 + 10b$       **3**    $c^2 - 4c$

**4**    $d^2 - 6d$       **5**    $x^2 + 5x$       **6**    $y^2 - 3y$

**7**    $z^2 - 7z$       **8**    $m^2 + 2m$       **9**    $n^2 - n$

**10**    $u^2 - \frac{1}{2}u$       **11**    $v^2 + \frac{1}{4}v$       **12**    $h^2 + \frac{2}{3}h$

**13**    $k^2 - 1\frac{1}{3}k$       **14**    $g^2 - 4\frac{2}{3}g$       **15**    $a^2 + \frac{3}{5}a$

**16**    $b^2 - \frac{4}{5}b$       **17**    $c^2 - 1\frac{1}{2}c$       **18**    $m^2 - 8m$

Solve the following quadratic equations. Some of them factorise, so if you can see the factors, solve them that way, but otherwise you will have to complete the square. Do not put your answers into decimal form.

**19**    $a^2 - 4a - 21 = 0$          **20**    $b^2 - b - 12 = 0$

**21**    $c^2 - 4c - 2 = 0$          **22**    $d^2 + 2d - 2 = 0$

**23**    $n^2 + 4n + 4 = 0$          **24**    $p^2 - 10p - 15 = 0$

**25**    $q^2 + 10q + 22 = 0$        **26**    $t^2 - 6t + 9 = 0$

**27**    $m^2 + 6m + 7 = 0$         **28**    $2e^2 - e - 1 = 0$

**29**    $3m^2 = 6m + 2$            **30**    $2d^2 - 4d + 1 = 0$

Use any method to solve the following quadratic equations. Do not put your answers into decimal form.

**31**    $y^2 + y - 8 = 0$           **32**    $x^2 - x - 6 = 0$

**33**    $a^2 - 6a - 3 = 0$          **34**    $2b^2 - 8b - 11 = 0$

**35**    $2c^2 - 3c - 9 = 0$         **36**    $x^2 - 10x + 23 = 0$

**37**    $h^2 = 3h + 40$            **38**    $4c^2 - 8c + 1 = 0$

**39**  $d^2 = 12d - 35$     **40**  $e^2 = 3e + 11$

**41**  $x^2 + 5x = 15$     **42**  $3m^2 - 5m + 2 = 0$

**43**  $4h^2 = 8h + 3$     **44**  $3k^2 = 9k - 2$

**45**  $b^2 = 11b + 26$     **46**  $5f^2 = 20f - 8$

**47**  $5e^2 + 15e + 1 = 0$     **48**  $y^2 - 9y + 15 = 0$

Find the maximum or minimum value of each of the following expressions by completing the square.

**49**  $a^2 - 4a - 21$     **50**  $b^2 - b - 12$

**51**  $c^2 - 4c - 2$     **52**  $d^2 + 2d - 2$

**53**  $n^2 + 4n + 4$     **54**  $p^2 - 10p - 15$

**55**  $2x - x^2$     **56**  $3 - 2y - y^2$

**57**  $5 + 4z - z^2$     **58**  $5 + 4z - 2z^2$

# 13    Linear inequalities

Solving inequalities is, in many ways, just like solving equations. You carry out operations to both sides of the inequality to make it simpler at each stage. However, there is one important difference.

● When you multiply or divide by a negative number, you must change the direction of the inequality.

**1**  Solve the inequality $x - 4 < 9$.

$$x - 4 < 9$$

Add 4 to both sides.    $x < 13$

**2**  Solve the inequality $4 - 2x \leq 8$.

Method 1

$$4 - 2x \leq 8$$

Subtract 4 from both sides.    $-2x \leq 4$

Divide both sides by $-2$, remembering to change the direction of the inequality.    $x \geq -2$

Method 2

$$4 - 2x \leq 8$$

Subtract 4 from both sides.    $-2x \leq 4$

Add $2x$ to both sides, to make the coefficient of $x$ positive.    $0 \leq 2x + 4$

Subtract 4 from both sides.    $-4 \leq 2x$

Divide by the positive number 2.    $-2 \leq x$

Rewrite the inequality.    $x \geq -2$

**3**    Solve the inequality $3(x+4) > 2(2-3x)+\frac{1}{2}$.

|  |  |
|---|---|
|  | $3(x+4) > 2(2-3x)+\frac{1}{2}$ |
| Multiply both sides by 2 to eliminate the fractions. | $6(x+4) > 4(2-3x)+1$ |
| Multiply out the brackets. | $6x+24 > 8-12x+1$ |
| Simplify the right-hand side. | $6x+24 > 9-12x$ |
| Add $12x$ to both sides. | $18x+24 > 9$ |
| Subtract 24 from both sides. | $18x > -15$ |
| Divide both sides by 18. | $x > -\frac{5}{6}$ |

## Exercise 13

Solve the following inequalities.

| | | | |
|---|---|---|---|
| **1** | $x-2 < 3$ | **2** | $x-3 \le 5$ |
| **3** | $x+3 > 6$ | **4** | $x+1 \ge 3$ |
| **5** | $3-x < 1$ | **6** | $2-x \le 3$ |
| **7** | $2 > x-4$ | **8** | $2x \ge 6$ |
| **9** | $2 > x-4$ | **10** | $3x-1 \le 2$ |
| **11** | $-2x < -6$ | **12** | $1-3x \le 4$ |
| **13** | $3x+4 < 1$ | **14** | $5x+6 \ge 3+2x$ |
| **15** | $5-2x > 1$ | **16** | $5-5x \le x-4$ |
| **17** | $5x-2 > 19-2x$ | **18** | $2(x-3) \ge 5$ |
| **19** | $2(x+3) > 3(2-x)$ | **20** | $2(x-3) \ge 5x$ |
| **21** | $\frac{1}{4}(x-3) < \frac{1}{3}x$ | **22** | $\frac{1}{2}(3x-2) \le \frac{1}{3}(x+4)$ |
| **23** | $-2(x-3) > -3(x+2)$ | **24** | $\frac{x}{3}+\frac{1}{4} \le \frac{x}{5}-\frac{1}{2}$ |

# 14 Multiplication and division

You multiply algebraic expressions by an extension of the rule for multiplying out brackets. It helps to organise the work carefully to avoid errors. People often use a layout similar to the one for long multiplication of numbers.

Notice the similarity of this process to long multiplication in arithmetic. A separate column is kept for each power of $x$.

**1** Multiply $2x^3 - 3x^2 + 2x - 3$ by $2x + 3$.

The row starting $4x^4$ comes from multiplying $2x^3 - 3x^2 + 2x - 3$ by $2x$.

The row starting $+6x^3$ comes from multiplying it by 3.

Then add the columns to get the product in the bottom row.

$$2x^3 - 3x^2 + 2x - 3$$
$$2x + 3$$
$$\overline{4x^4 - 6x^3 + 4x^2 - 6x}$$
$$+6x^3 - 9x^2 + 6x - 9$$
$$\overline{4x^4 \qquad -5x^2 \qquad -9}$$

The product is $4x^4 - 5x^2 - 9$.

**2** Multiply $x^2 + 2xy + 4y^2$ by $2x - 3y$.

This is very similar to the first worked example.

Multiply $x^2 + 2xy + 4y^2$ first by $2x$, then by $-3y$.

Then add the results to get the product.

$$x^2 + 2xy + 4y^2$$
$$2x - 3y$$
$$\overline{2x^3 + 4x^2y + 8xy^2}$$
$$-3x^2y - 6xy^2 - 12y^3$$
$$\overline{2x^3 - x^3y + 2xy^2 - 12y^3}$$

The product is
$$2x^3 - x^3y + 2xy^2 - 12y^3.$$

**3**   Multiply $x + y - 2$ by $x - y + 2$.

Once again, terms which are like one another are arranged underneath one another in columns.

$$x + y - 2$$
$$x - y + 2$$
$$x^2 + xy - 2x$$
$$\phantom{x^2} - xy \phantom{+2x} - y^2 + 2y$$
$$\phantom{x^2 - xy} + 2x \phantom{- y^2} + 2y - 4$$
$$x^2 \phantom{+ xy + 2x} - y^2 + 4y + 4$$

Then add the results to get the product.

The product is $x^2 - y^2 + 4y + 4$.

**4**   Divide $-18d^3 + 17d - 11$ by $3d - 2$.

Notice the gap left for the 'missing' $d^2$ term.

Start by dividing $3d$ into $-18d^3$; result $-6d^2$.

Multiply $3d - 2$ by $-6d^2$ and subtract the result from $-18d^3$ giving $-12d^2$.

Now divide $3d - 2$ into $-12d^2 + 17d$; result $-4d$; and so on.

$$
\begin{array}{r}
-6d^2 - 4d + 3 \\
3d - 2 \overline{)\ -18d^3 \phantom{00} + 17d - 11} \\
\underline{-18d^3 + 12d^2} \phantom{000000} \\
-12d^2 + 17d \phantom{00} \\
\underline{-12d^2 + 8d} \phantom{00} \\
9d - 11 \\
\underline{9d - 6} \\
-5
\end{array}
$$

The quotient is $-6d^2 - 4d + 3$, and the remainder is $-5$.

**5**  Divide $5a^3 - 3b^3 + 19ab^2 - 21a^2b$ by $a^2 + 3b^2 - 4ab$.

$$
\begin{array}{r}
5a \quad - \quad b \\
a^2 - 4ab + 3b^2 \overline{\smash{)}\; 5a^3 - 21a^2b + 19ab^2 - 3b^3} \\
\underline{5a^3 - 20a^2b + 15ab^2} \\
-\ a^2b + 4ab^2 - 3b^3 \\
\underline{-\ a^2b + 4ab^2 - 3b^3}
\end{array}
$$

The quotient is $5a - b$, and there is no remainder.

## Exercise 14

Multiply

|  |  |  |  |
|---|---|---|---|
| **1** | $x^2 - 3x + 1$ | by | $2x + 3$ |
| **2** | $2y^2 + y - 3$ | by | $3y - 4$ |
| **3** | $3z^2 - 5z - 2$ | by | $3z + 5$ |
| **4** | $a^2 + a - 3$ | by | $2a + 6$ |
| **5** | $2b^2 - 3b - 1$ | by | $3b - 2$ |
| **6** | $m^2 - mn + n^2$ | by | $3m + 2n$ |
| **7** | $3a^2 - ab - b^2$ | by | $2a - 2b$ |
| **8** | $x^2 - 2xy + 3y^2$ | by | $2x - y$ |
| **9** | $c^2 + 3cd - d^2$ | by | $2c + d$ |
| **10** | $2h^2 + 4hk - k^2$ | by | $3h - 6k$ |
| **11** | $m + n + 1$ | by | $m - n - 1$ |
| **12** | $u + v - 1$ | by | $u + v + 1$ |
| **13** | $2a - b + 3$ | by | $2a + b - 3$ |
| **14** | $2 + 3m - 2n$ | by | $3 + 3m + 2n$ |
| **15** | $m^3 + 2 + m - 3m^2$ | by | $3m + 1$ |
| **16** | $2n^2 - 1 + 3n + n^3$ | by | $2n - 3$ |
| **17** | $a^3 - 2a^2 - 2a + 5$ | by | $a^2 - a + 2$ |
| **18** | $2u + v - 3w$ | by | $u - 2v - 3w$ |

**19** $c - 2d - 5e$          by    $c + 2d - 5e$
**20** $a^3 + a^2d - d^3$      by    $a^2 - ad + d^2$

Divide

**21** $a^3 - a^2 - 3a + 2$          by    $a - 2$
**22** $m^3 + 2m^2 - m + 6$          by    $m + 3$
**23** $2x^3 + 7x^2 - 2x - 10$       by    $2x + 3$
**24** $3u^3 - 7u^2 + 11u - 7$       by    $3u - 1$
**25** $2m^3 - 9m^2n + 5mn^2 + 6n^3$ by    $2m - 3n$
**26** $2x^3 + 3x^2y - 4xy^2 + y^3$  by    $2x - y$
**27** $2b^3 + 7b^2c - 6c^3$         by    $2b + 3c$
**28** $a^3 - 7ad^2 + 6d^3$          by    $a + 3d$
**29** $9x^3 - 16x - 10$             by    $3x + 2$
**30** $y^2 + 15 + 6y^3$             by    $2y + 3$
**31** $3a^3 - 7a^2b + 4b^3$         by    $3a^2 - ab - 2b^2$
**32** $4m^3 - 7mu^2 + 3u^3$         by    $2m^2 + mu - 3u^2$
**33** $9h^3 + 8k^3 - 22hk^2$        by    $3h - 4k$
**34** $31m^2n - 9n^3 + 10m^3$       by    $5m + 3n$
**35** $6b^2 - 1 - 11b + 9b^3$       by    $3b^2 + 4b - 1$
**36** $8 - 11a^2 + 6a^3 - 9a$       by    $2a^2 - 3a - 4$
**37** $m^3 - n^3$                   by    $m - n$
**38** $m^3 + n^3$                   by    $m^2 - mn + n^2$
**39** $6u^3 + 4v^3 - 23uv^2 + 7u^2v$ by   $2u^2 - v^2 + 5uv$
**40** $19mn^2 - 17m^2n + 4m^3 - 5n^3$ by  $m^2 + n^2 - 3mn$

# 15 Indices

When $x$ and $y$ are positive whole numbers the rules for indices are

- $a^x \times a^y = a^{x+y}$      Rule 1

- $a^x \div a^y = a^{x-y}$      Rule 2

- $\left(a^x\right)^y = a^{xy}$.      Rule 3

Meanings can also be found for powers when $x$ and $y$ are any numbers, positive, negative or fractions.

These rules, which won't be proved are:

- $a^{\frac{1}{n}} = \sqrt[n]{a}$      Rule 4

- $a^0 = 1$      Rule 5

- $a^{-n} = \dfrac{1}{a^n}$      Rule 6

- $a^{\frac{x}{y}} = \sqrt[y]{a^x}$ or $\left(\sqrt[y]{a}\right)^x$      Rule 7

**1**   Simplify $3a^2 \times 2a^4$.

This means $3 \times a^2 \times 2 \times a^4$, so multiply the numbers and use Rule 1.

$$3a^2 \times 2a^4$$
$$= 6a^6$$

**2**   Simplify $3a \times (2a)^2$.

This means $3a \times 2a \times 2a$, so multiply the numbers and use Rule 1.

$$3a \times (2a)^2$$
$$= 12a^3$$

**3**  Simplify $25^{\frac{1}{2}}$.

Using Rule 4, this means $\sqrt{25}$.

$$25^{\frac{1}{2}}$$
$$= 5$$

**4**  Simplify $16^{\frac{3}{2}}$.

Using Rule 7, this means $\left(\sqrt{16}\right)^3$.

$$16^{\frac{3}{2}}$$
$$= 4^3 = 64$$

**5**  Simplify $3^{-4}$.

Using Rule 6, this means $\dfrac{1}{3^4}$.

$$3^{-4}$$
$$= \frac{1}{3^4} = \frac{1}{81}$$

**6**  Simplify $9^{-\frac{3}{2}}$.

Using Rule 6, this means $\dfrac{1}{9^{\frac{3}{2}}}$.
Then use Rule 7.

$$9^{-\frac{3}{2}}$$
$$= \frac{1}{9^{\frac{3}{2}}} = \frac{1}{3^3} = \frac{1}{27}$$

**7**  Simplify $3x^0$.

This means $3 \times x^0$. Then use
Rule 5.

$$3x^0$$
$$= 3 \times 1 = 3$$

# *Exercise 15*

Simplify the following expressions.

| | | | | | |
|---|---|---|---|---|---|
| **1** | $2a \times 3a^2$ | **2** | $2a \times (3a)^2$ | **3** | $(2a)^2 \times 3a$ |
| **4** | $4^{\frac{1}{2}}$ | **5** | $27^{\frac{1}{3}}$ | **6** | $125^{\frac{1}{3}}$ |
| **7** | $\sqrt[3]{2^6}$ | **8** | $8^{\frac{2}{3}}$ | **9** | $2^{-2}$ |
| **10** | $3^{-3}$ | **11** | $9^{\frac{1}{2}}$ | **12** | $9^{-\frac{1}{2}}$ |
| **13** | $\left(25a^2\right)^{\frac{1}{2}}$ | **14** | $2a^{-1}$ | **15** | $(2a)^{-1}$ |
| **16** | $4^{\frac{3}{2}}$ | **17** | $2^{-2} \times 2^3$ | **18** | $\left(2^2\right)^2$ |
| **19** | $10^{-2}$ | **20** | $\sqrt{1\frac{9}{16}}$ | **21** | $3a^{-2}$ |
| **22** | $(3a)^{-2}$ | **23** | $\sqrt{3^4}$ | **24** | $\left(a^2\right)^{-\frac{1}{2}}$ |
| **25** | $\left(\frac{1}{9}\right)^{-1}$ | **26** | $\left(\frac{1}{4}\right)^{-\frac{1}{2}}$ | **27** | $3^{\frac{1}{2}} \times 3^{\frac{3}{2}}$ |
| **28** | $\left(\frac{1}{27}\right)^{-\frac{2}{3}}$ | **29** | $3^{\frac{1}{2}} \times 3^{-\frac{3}{2}}$ | **30** | $0.04^{\frac{1}{2}}$ |
| **31** | $2a^{-1} \times 3a^2$ | **32** | $(2a)^{-1} \times 3a^2$ | **33** | $2a^{-1} \times (3a)^2$ |
| **34** | $16^{-\frac{3}{2}}$ | **35** | $2^{\frac{1}{2}} \times 2^{\frac{5}{2}}$ | **36** | $\left(2^6\right)^{-\frac{2}{3}}$ |
| **37** | $125^{-\frac{2}{3}}$ | **38** | $3^x \times 3^{-x}$ | **39** | $16^{-\frac{3}{4}}$ |
| **40** | $0.027^{\frac{2}{3}}$ | **41** | $2a \times 3a^{-2}$ | **42** | $2a \times (3a)^{-2}$ |
| **43** | $4^{-\frac{3}{2}}$ | **44** | $\left(\frac{8}{27}\right)^{-\frac{2}{3}}$ | **45** | $\frac{1}{3^{-2}}$ |
| **46** | $2 \times 2^{-3}$ | **47** | $\sqrt[3]{4^{1.5}}$ | **48** | $3^{n-1} \times 3^{1-n}$ |
| **49** | $64^{-\frac{5}{6}}$ | **50** | $\sqrt[3]{8a^{-6}}$ | **51** | $2x^{\frac{1}{2}} \times 3x^{-\frac{5}{2}}$ |
| **52** | $0.125^{-\frac{1}{3}}$ | **53** | $\left(\frac{16}{9}\right)^{-\frac{3}{2}}$ | **54** | $\sqrt[4]{16a^{-12}}$ |

**55** $4a^3b \times 3ab^{-2}$ **56** $4a^3b \times (3ab)^{-2}$ **57** $\sqrt{\left(125^2\right)^{-\frac{1}{3}}}$

**58** $\dfrac{75a^2b^{-2}}{5a^3b^{-3}}$ **59** $(2x)^{\frac{1}{2}} \times \left(2x^3\right)^{\frac{3}{2}}$ **60** $\left(\frac{18}{32}\right)^{-\frac{3}{2}}$

Re-write the following expressions using positive indices only.

**61** $a^{-2}$ **62** $b^{-1}$ **63** $c^{-\frac{2}{3}}$

**64** $xy^{-1}$ **65** $(xy)^{-1}$ **66** $a^{-2}b^3$

**67** $ab^{-3}$ **68** $(ab)^{-3}$ **69** $2x^{-\frac{1}{2}}$

**70** $3y^{-\frac{2}{5}}$

Solve for $x$ the following equations.

**71** $x^{\frac{1}{2}} = 2$ **72** $x^{\frac{1}{3}} = 3$ **73** $x^{-1} = 2$

**74** $x^{-2} = 9$ **75** $2x^3 = 54$ **76** $x^{-\frac{1}{2}} = 5$

**77** $x^{-\frac{3}{2}} = 9$ **78** $2x^{-3} = -16$ **79** $5x = 40x^{-\frac{1}{2}}$

**80** $x = 9\sqrt{9x^{\frac{1}{2}}}$

# 16   Revision exercises

**Revision  exercise  1**

1   Factorise $a^2 + 5a - 14$.

2   Solve the equation $\dfrac{a-8}{3} + \dfrac{a-3}{2} = 0$.

3   Solve the equation $3x^2 - 13x + 10 = 0$.

4   Factorise $x^2 - 25y^2$.

5   Solve the equation $\dfrac{5-x}{4} = \dfrac{1}{x}$.

6   Express as a single fraction $\dfrac{3m+2}{4} - \dfrac{2m+5}{3} + \dfrac{1}{6}$.

7   Solve the simultaneous equations $\begin{cases} 2x + 3y = 4 \\ 3x - y = -5 \end{cases}$

8   Solve for $l$ the equation $e = \dfrac{kl}{l+a}$.

9   Simplify $3^{x+y} \times 3^{x-y} \times 9^{-x}$.

10   Solve the inequality $2 - 3x < -10$.

**Revision  exercise  2**

1   Solve for $r$ the equation $V = \pi h^2 \left( r - \dfrac{h}{3} \right)$.

2   Factorise $a^2 - 2bc - 2ab + ac$.

3   Solve the equation $\dfrac{1}{x-1} + \dfrac{2}{2x-1} = \dfrac{6}{3x-1}$.

**4**  Solve the equation $\frac{1}{10}\left(\frac{7x}{2}+8\right)-\frac{4x-5}{3}=\frac{1}{2}$.

**5**  Solve the simultaneous equations $\begin{cases} 2x=3y+4 \\ x-2y+3=0 \end{cases}$

**6**  Simplify $9^{-\frac{3}{2}}$.

**7**  Solve the equation $\frac{10}{x-2}-\frac{10}{x+3}=1$.

**8**  Solve the inequality $4(x-1)\le 3(x-1)$.

**9**  Factorise $9x^2-16y^2$.

**10**  Simplify $\frac{1}{2}(x+2y)-\frac{1}{3}(2x-5y)$.

## Revision exercise 3

**1**  Solve the equation $(x-1)^2=x-1$.

**2**  Factorise $4x^2-17xy+4y^2$.

**3**  Factorise $6ax-6y-9ay+4x$.

**4**  Solve for $H$ the equation $E=\frac{2Hg-V^2}{2Hg}$.

**5**  Solve the equation $3x^2-5x+1=0$ giving your answers correct to 2 decimal places.

**6**  Express $\frac{3-x}{2}-\frac{x-5}{4}$ as a single fraction.

**7**  Solve the equation $10\left(3+\frac{1}{x}\right)=29$.

**8**  Solve the equation $10x^2+10=29x$.

**9** Solve the simultaneous equations $\begin{cases} 4x - 5y = 2 \\ 5x + 4y = 23 \end{cases}$

**10** Simplify $\sqrt{x^2 y} \div xy^2$.

## Revision exercise 4

**1** Simplify $(3a)^2 \times 4a$.

**2** Solve the simultaneous equations $x - y = 2x - 3y = 5$.

**3** Solve for $d$ the equation $v = \sqrt{gd\left(1 + \dfrac{3h}{d}\right)}$.

**4** Solve the equation $2x^2 - 4x - 3 = 0$ giving your answers correct to 2 decimal places.

**5** Solve the equation $(x - 2)(x - 3) = 2$.

**6** Express $\dfrac{2}{x} + \dfrac{1}{2}$ as a single fraction.

**7** Factorise completely $x^4 - y^4$.

**8** Solve the equation $\dfrac{x - 1}{2} - \dfrac{2(x - 2)}{3} = 1$.

**9** Solve the inequality $\frac{1}{2}(3x - 1) > \frac{2}{3}(4x - 1)$.

**10** Find the remainder when $x^3 - 2x + 1$ is divided by $x - 3$.

## Revision exercise 5

**1** Multiply $x^2 - 2x + 4$ by $x + 2$.

**2** Factorise $a^2 + 2ab + b^2 - c^2$.

**3** Solve the equation $\dfrac{x-1}{2} - \dfrac{2(x-2)}{3} = -1$.

**4** Simplify $\left(x^3 y^2\right)^{-\frac{1}{2}} \times (xy)^2$.

**5** Solve the equation $-x^2 + 12x - 3 = 0$ giving your answers correct to 2 decimal places.

**6** Solve the equation $\dfrac{2x}{x+3} - \dfrac{x-1}{x+1} = \dfrac{1}{2}$.

**7** Eliminate $E$ from the equations $E = 2c\left(1 + \dfrac{1}{m}\right) = 3k\left(1 - \dfrac{2}{m}\right)$ and solve the resulting equation for $m$.

**8** Find the quotient and the remainder when $x^4$ is divided by $x^2 - 2x + 2$.

**9** Factorise $12x^2 - 7xy - 12y^2$.

**10** Solve the inequality $-3(x+1) \geq \frac{1}{2}x$.

# 17 Answers

## Exercise 2, page 5

| | | | | | |
|---|---|---|---|---|---|
| **1** | $7d$ | **2** | $6e$ | **3** | $6n$ |
| **4** | $4a+14b$ | **5** | $3h+6$ | **6** | $7x+5y-4$ |
| **7** | $4x+9y$ | **8** | $4a+9b$ | **9** | $f+2g$ |
| **10** | $2m+5n+9$ | **11** | $x+4$ | **12** | $3a+b+3c$ |
| **13** | $3h+5k+2$ | **14** | $3n+3$ | **15** | $a+3b+3c$ |
| **16** | $3q+4r+3s$ | **17** | $7xy$ | **18** | $4ab$ |
| **19** | $8hk$ | **20** | $10ab+7bc$ | **21** | $2cd$ |
| **22** | $xy$ | **23** | $3ab+3bc$ | **24** | $2ab+3bc$ |
| **25** | $6fg+3gh$ | **26** | $uv+2vw$ | **27** | $3ab+2bc+cd$ |
| **28** | $11mn-8mu-6vu$ | | | **29** | $3ab+2cd+2ac$ |
| **30** | $4p-2q+3r+2s$ | | | **31** | $5a^2+7a+8$ |
| **32** | $6b^2+2b+1$ | **33** | $2c^2+3c+5$ | **34** | $x^2+5x+3$ |
| **35** | $7y^2+4y+3$ | **36** | $2z^3+5z^2+8z+4$ | | |
| **37** | $15m$ | **38** | $32a$ | **39** | $21h$ |
| **40** | $5k$ | **41** | $4x$ | **42** | $11n$ |
| **43** | $17p$ | **44** | $12a+5$ | **45** | $14b-3$ |
| **46** | $3+10m$ | **47** | $13x$ | **48** | $7y$ |
| **49** | $21-14a$ | **50** | $0$ | **51** | $3a$ |
| **52** | $5t+1$ | **53** | $11x$ | **54** | $5ab$ |
| **55** | $7mn$ | **56** | $10u$ | **57** | $6xy$ |
| **58** | $0$ | **59** | $12ab$ | **60** | $3a+4b$ |
| **61** | $pq$ | **62** | $5x$ | **63** | $7cd$ |
| **64** | $15m^2$ | **65** | $28n^2$ | **66** | $40u$ |
| **67** | $0$ | **68** | $2a$ | | |

## Exercise 3, page 9

| | | | | | |
|---|---|---|---|---|---|
| **1** | $\frac{3}{8}$ | **2** | $\frac{5}{7}$ | **3** | $\frac{1}{5}$ |
| **4** | $\frac{3}{4}$ | **5** | $\frac{1}{3}$ | **6** | $\frac{3}{4}$ |
| **7** | $\frac{x}{4y}$ | **8** | $\frac{4a}{5c}$ | **9** | $\frac{a}{3}$ |

**10** $\dfrac{2k}{3h}$     **11** $\dfrac{3a}{4}$     **12** $\dfrac{3}{4n}$

**13** $\dfrac{4m}{5n}$     **14** $\dfrac{3}{4x}$     **15** $\dfrac{z}{y}$

**16** $\dfrac{8a}{11}$     **17** $\dfrac{2b}{8} = \dfrac{b}{4}$     **18** $\dfrac{6c}{5}$

**19** $\dfrac{11x}{12}$     **20** $\dfrac{10m-9n}{15}$     **21** $\dfrac{20a-9b}{24}$

**22** $\dfrac{a+2b}{m}$     **23** $\dfrac{2x}{a}$     **24** $\dfrac{10}{mn}$

**25** $\dfrac{2c+3d}{uvw}$     **26** $\dfrac{8a-3b+5c}{10}$     **27** $\dfrac{a}{4}$

**28** $\dfrac{6a-8b+9c}{12}$     **29** $\dfrac{4a+x}{4}$     **30** $\dfrac{10a-9c}{24}$

**31** $\dfrac{3c+8d-10e}{12}$     **32** $\dfrac{5u-2d}{5}$     **33** $\dfrac{4n-3m}{mn}$

**34** $\dfrac{3m-2n}{6a}$     **35** $\dfrac{2b-5a}{abu}$     **36** $\dfrac{4e+3a}{ace}$

**37** $\dfrac{3x+5n-2m}{mnx}$     **38** $\dfrac{pc-qb+ra}{abc}$     **39** $\dfrac{2a}{3}$

**40** $\dfrac{15}{2}$     **41** $\dfrac{18}{a}$     **42** $\dfrac{3x}{8}$

**43** $\dfrac{2m}{9}$     **44** $\dfrac{8m}{15e}$     **45** $\dfrac{5h}{6m}$

**46** $\dfrac{9a}{4}$     **47** $\dfrac{24cm}{35b}$     **48** $\dfrac{3amx}{y}$

**49** $\dfrac{7}{3}$     **50** $\dfrac{9}{4}$     **51** $\dfrac{a}{8}$

**52** $\dfrac{3a}{4b}$

## Exercise 4, page 13

**1** $h+k-m+n$     **2** $h-k-m+n$     **3** $a-b+c$

**4** $5a+b-5c$     **5** $4x-3y-2$     **6** $6-p-3q+7r$

**7** $3m+6h-k-5n$     **8** $4a-b+3c-7$     **9** $4a-5x+2y+3b$

**10** $3e+f-2g+h$     **11** $2a-2b$     **12** $4m+3n$

**13** $3x+y$     **14** $-x+5y$     **15** $3n$

**16** $3u$     **17** $2u-5v$     **18** $7a-7$

| 19 | $-2m-2$ | 20 | $5u-3v$ | 21 | $2a^2+7a-4$ |
|---|---|---|---|---|---|
| 22 | $-x-6y+4$ | 23 | $p-3q$ | 24 | $-b$ |
| 25 | $zw-yz$ | 26 | $a^2-6a+6$ | 27 | $a-2b-3c+3$ |
| 28 | $7g+2h-8k$ | 29 | $-2e^2+2e-2$ | 30 | $lm-mn+nl$ |
| 31 | $3u+3v+3w$ | 32 | $-4l+4m+4n$ | 33 | $2x+6y+4z$ |
| 34 | $15a+5b-10c$ | 35 | $15p-6q-9r+12s$ | | |
| 36 | $-6c-9d+15$ | 37 | $u-4v+3$ | 38 | $9c-15d-3e$ |
| 39 | $6m+2n-3u-6v$ | | | | |
| 40 | $15a-20b+6c+10d$ | | | 41 | $5a+4b$ |
| 42 | $3x+6y$ | 43 | $2u+5v$ | 44 | $-d-3e$ |
| 45 | $2n$ | 46 | $2u-6v$ | 47 | $5a-3b$ |
| 48 | $12m-2$ | 49 | $12m-8$ | 50 | $7h+20k$ |
| 51 | $5b-2c$ | 52 | $-15b$ | 53 | $-2x-5y$ |
| 54 | $2u+3v$ | 55 | $a+b-4c$ | 56 | $7a+9b-4c$ |
| 57 | $-1$ | 58 | $0$ | 59 | $6a$ |
| 60 | $-4u-7v-13w$ | 61 | $4x+10$ | 62 | $3x+3$ |
| 63 | $-5x+35$ | 64 | $4x+32$ | 65 | $x^2-4xy-2y^2$ |
| 66 | $3a^2+6ab+3b^2$ | | | | |

## Exercise 5, page 16

| 1 | $\dfrac{3a+1}{2}$ | 2 | $\dfrac{5b-2}{3}$ | 3 | $\dfrac{2c-4}{5}$ |
|---|---|---|---|---|---|
| 4 | $\dfrac{x-3}{2}$ | 5 | $\dfrac{7z-5}{4}$ | 6 | $\dfrac{-7n+10}{12}$ |
| 7 | $\dfrac{17u-15}{12}$ | 8 | $\dfrac{u-7v}{24}$ | 9 | $\dfrac{11a-2}{4}$ |
| 10 | $\dfrac{b+1}{2}$ | 11 | $\dfrac{-x-y}{3}$ | 12 | $\dfrac{13c-12d}{30}$ |
| 13 | $\dfrac{2h+3k}{3}$ | 14 | $\dfrac{11a}{18}$ | 15 | $\dfrac{a-17b}{6}$ |
| 16 | $\dfrac{29u+8v}{12}$ | 17 | $\dfrac{6m+25n}{12}$ | 18 | $\dfrac{56b-33c}{24}$ |
| 19 | $\dfrac{-a+3b-2c}{2}$ | 20 | $\dfrac{3u-11v+7}{5}$ | 21 | $\dfrac{2m+5}{4}$ |

*Help yourself to algebra*

**22** $\dfrac{5a - 2b - 3c}{3}$    **23** $\dfrac{13x + 6}{15}$    **24** $\dfrac{6a - 7b}{2}$

**25** $\dfrac{3m - 8n}{2}$

## Exercise 6, page 21

| | | | | | |
|---|---|---|---|---|---|
| **1** | 5 | **2** | 3 | **3** | 1 |
| **4** | $5\frac{1}{2}$ | **5** | $\frac{2}{3}$ | **6** | $\frac{3}{4}$ |
| **7** | 4 | **8** | 3 | **9** | $2\frac{1}{2}$ |
| **10** | $2\frac{1}{3}$ | **11** | 7 | **12** | 1 |
| **13** | 0 | **14** | $4\frac{2}{3}$ | **15** | $\frac{3}{5}$ |
| **16** | $2\frac{1}{5}$ | **17** | 6 | **18** | 0 |
| **19** | 8 | **20** | 15 | **21** | $2\frac{1}{2}$ |
| **22** | 1 | **23** | 2 | **24** | $1\frac{1}{2}$ |
| **25** | 3 | **26** | 5 | **27** | 6 |
| **28** | $1\frac{2}{3}$ | **29** | $1\frac{1}{3}$ | **30** | $2\frac{3}{5}$ |
| **31** | 2 | **32** | $1\frac{1}{2}$ | **33** | 10 |
| **34** | 3 | **35** | 7 | **36** | 3 |
| **37** | $\frac{3}{4}$ | **38** | 2 | **39** | $1\frac{3}{4}$ |
| **40** | 2 | **41** | 4 | **42** | $5\frac{1}{8}$ |
| **43** | $1\frac{1}{2}$ | **44** | 2 | **45** | 4 |
| **46** | 5 | **47** | $3\frac{2}{5}$ | **48** | 4 |
| **49** | 4 | **50** | $5\frac{2}{3}$ | **51** | $1\frac{2}{5}$ |
| **52** | 2 | **53** | $\frac{2}{3}$ | **54** | $\frac{3}{8}$ |

## Exercise 7, page 26

| | | | | | |
|---|---|---|---|---|---|
| **1** | $x = 1, y = 4$ | **2** | $x = 3, y = 2$ | **3** | $x = -1, y = 2$ |
| **4** | $x = 3, y = 1$ | **5** | $x = -1, y = -1$ | **6** | $x = 2, y = 2$ |

**7**  $x = 1, y = 3$      **8**  $x = -2, y = -3$      **9**  $x = 2, y = -4$

**10**  $x = 0, y = 3$      **11**  $x = 0, y = -2$      **12**  $x = -3, y = 0$

**13**  $x = 1, y = -5$      **14**  $x = 2, y = -3$      **15**  $a = 2\frac{1}{2}, b = 1$

**16**  $h = 2, k = 1\frac{1}{2}$      **17**  $p = -1, q = -2$      **18**  $r = -2, s = 11$

**19**  $x = 12, y = -5$      **20**  $a = 3, b = 4$      **21**  $x = 1, y = -3$

**22**  $u = -2, v = 1$      **23**  $d = -2, e = 2$      **24**  $x = 1\frac{1}{3}, y = 3$

**25**  $f = 2\frac{1}{3}, g = 1\frac{1}{2}$    **26**  $e = 2\frac{1}{2}, f = -2$    **27**  $p = -3\frac{1}{2}, q = 3$

**28**  $m = -1\frac{3}{4}, n = -2\frac{1}{3}$                  **29**  $h = -2\frac{3}{5}, k = 4\frac{1}{10}$

**30**  $x = 2\frac{1}{2}, y = -3\frac{1}{4}$                  **31**  $x = 3, y = 4$

**32**  $x = 2, y = -3$      **33**  $x = 2, y = 5$      **34**  $a = -3, b = 4$

**35**  $f = 4, g = 3$      **36**  $x = 1, y = 2$      **37**  $m = 3, n = -1$

**38**  $x = 2, y = 2$      **39**  $m = 3, n = -1$      **40**  $f = -1, g = 2\frac{1}{2}$

## Exercise 8, page 28

**1**  $ab - ad - bc + cd$          **2**  $xp - xq + yp - yq$

**3**  $ac + 2ad - 2bc - 4bd$      **4**  $2xp + 4xq - yp - 2yq$

**5**  $2h^2 - 5hk + 3k^2$          **6**  $ab - ac - bc + c^2$

**7**  $a^2 + 7a + 12$      **8**  $b^2 + 7b + 10$      **9**  $m^2 + m - 6$

**10**  $n^2 - 5n - 14$      **11**  $x^2 + 4x + 4$      **12**  $y^2 - 3y - 4$

**13**  $c^2 + 3c - 10$      **14**  $d^2 - 7d + 12$      **15**  $p^2 - 7p + 10$

**16**  $x^2 - 8x + 16$      **17**  $y^2 + 8y + 7$      **18**  $a^2 + 2a - 24$

**19**  $b^2 - 10b + 21$      **20**  $c^2 + 4c - 5$      **21**  $6 + 5d + d^2$

**22**  $10 + 3x - x^2$      **23**  $12 - 7y + y^2$      **24**  $m^2 + 5mn + 6n^2$

**25**  $a^2 - ab - 6b^2$      **26**  $x^2 - 7xy + 12y^2$    **27**  $p^2 + 4pq + 4q^2$

**28**  $m^2 + 2mn - 15n^2$                  **29**  $2a^2 + 7a - 15$

**30**  $3x^2 - 2x - 8$    **31**  $6h^2 + hk - 2k^2$    **32**  $15x^2 + 26xy + 8y^2$

**33**  $9a^2 - 12ab + 4b^2$             **34**  $25h^2 + 10hk + k^2$

**35**  $10a^2 - 19ab + 6b^2$

## Exercise 9, page 33

| | | |
|---|---|---|
| **1** $3(x-2y)$ | **2** $p(p+2)$ | **3** $q(p-r)$ |
| **4** $a(2-b)$ | **5** $2c(1+2c)$ | **6** $p(a+b)$ |
| **7** $m(3+u-v)$ | **8** $a(2-3x-y)$ | **9** $x(3-a+b)$ |
| **10** $p(4m-3n-5)$ | **11** $(a+b)(m+1)$ | **12** $(a-b)(n+2)$ |
| **13** $x(a-b+4c)$ | **14** $(5x-2y)(a-b)$ | **15** $(3h+2k)(5u-v)$ |
| **16** $m(u-v+m)$ | **17** $d(3h+k-4d)$ | **18** $a(5a+b-c)$ |
| **19** $(m+n)(x+y)$ | **20** $(h-k)(u+v)$ | **21** $(a+2b)(m+n)$ |
| **22** $(2c-d)(e-2f)$ | **23** $(a+1)(m-n)$ | **24** $(a+1)(a^2+1)$ |
| **25** $(3s+5t)(x-y)$ | **26** $(k+3n)(h-2m)$ | **27** $(2k-3l)(g+h)$ |
| **28** $(3c-2d)(e-2f)$ | | **29** $(a+3)(a+5)$ |
| **30** $(b-2)(b-5)$ | **31** $(c+7)(c-3)$ | **32** $(d-7)(d+2)$ |
| **33** $(e+4)(e-2)$ | **34** $(w+3)(w+2)$ | **35** $(x+6)(x-1)$ |
| **36** $(y-2)(y-3)$ | **37** $(z-6)(z+1)$ | **38** $(2d+1)(d+1)$ |
| **39** $(2e-1)(e-1)$ | **40** $(2f+1)(f-1)$ | **41** $(x-2)(x+2)$ |
| **42** No factors | **43** $(2x-3)(2x+3)$ | **44** $(a+5)(a+2)$ |
| **45** $(a+5b)(a+2b)$ | **46** $(ab+5)(ab+2)$ | **47** $(x-5y)(x+3y)$ |
| **48** $(m+12)(m-2)$ | **49** $(n-12)(n+2)$ | **50** $(v-8)(v-3)$ |
| **51** $(m+7)(m-3)$ | **52** $(m+7n)(m-3n)$ | **53** $(mn+7)(mn-3)$ |
| **54** $(3a-1)(a-1)$ | **55** $(3b-2)(b+1)$ | **56** No factors |
| **57** $(x-1)(x+1)$ | **58** $(1-y)(1+y)$ | **59** $(3-2c)(3+2c)$ |
| **60** $(5k-4)(5k+4)$ | **61** $3(1-x)(1+x)$ | **62** $(9-w)(9+w)$ |
| **63** No factors | | |

## Exercise 10, page 39

| | | |
|---|---|---|
| **1** $x=b-a$ | **2** $x=a-b$ | **3** $x=\dfrac{b}{a}$ |
| **4** $x=\dfrac{c}{a+b}$ | **5** $x=\dfrac{b}{1-a}$ | **6** $x=\dfrac{a}{b}$ |
| **7** $x=\dfrac{a}{c-b}$ | **8** $x=a(c-b)$ | **9** $x=\dfrac{ab}{a+b}$ |

**10** $x = a + b$     **11** $x = \dfrac{c}{a} - b$     **12** $x = \dfrac{bc}{a - b}$

**13** $x = \dfrac{ab}{a + c}$     **14** $x = \dfrac{6ab}{5}$     **15** $x = \dfrac{bc}{a}$

**16** $x = b - \dfrac{a}{c}$     **17** $x = \dfrac{b(3a - 2)}{2a + 3}$     **18** $x = a^2$

**19** $x = \dfrac{a^2}{2}$     **20** $x = \dfrac{a^2}{4}$     **21** $x = 2a^2$

**22** $x = 4a^2$     **23** $x = \dfrac{b^2}{a^2}$     **24** $x = \dfrac{b^2}{a}$

**25** $x = ab^3$     **26** $x = \pm a^2$     **27** $x = \pm \sqrt{a}$

**28** $x = b^2 - a$     **29** $x = (b - a)^2$     **30** $x = \pm \sqrt{b^2 - a^2}$

**31** $x = \pm 2a\sqrt{2}$     **32** $x = a - \dfrac{b}{2}$     **33** $x = 1 + \dfrac{b^2}{a^2}$

**34** $x = \left(\dfrac{b + 1}{a}\right)^2$     **35** $x = \dfrac{a}{a - b}$     **36** $x = 0$ if $a \neq -b$

**37** $x = b - a$     **38** $x = a^2 + ab + b^2$     **39** $x = -\dfrac{a + b}{2}$

**40** $x = \pm \dfrac{a}{b}\sqrt{b^2 - y^2}$     **41** $x = 2a + b$

**42** $x = \pm \sqrt{b^2 - a^2}$     **43** $x = \dfrac{3b}{4}$     **44** $x = a$

**45** $x = -a$     **46** $x = \dfrac{2ab}{2a - b}$     **47** $x = \dfrac{b}{2}$

**48** $x = -\dfrac{a^2}{b}$     **49** $x = 2a$     **50** $x = a$ or $x = a + b$

**51** $N = PD - 2$     **52** $b = \dfrac{kv}{k + rt}$     **53** $r = \dfrac{c}{2\pi}$

**54** $W = \dfrac{P - b}{a}$     **55** $n = \dfrac{2s}{a + l}$; $l = \dfrac{2s - an}{n}$

**56** $P = \dfrac{100A}{100 + RT}$; $T = \dfrac{100(A - P)}{PR}$     **57** $h = \dfrac{S}{2\pi r} - r$

**58** $s = \dfrac{v^2 - u^2}{2a}$; $u = \pm \sqrt{v^2 - 2as}$     **59** $W = \dfrac{LaP}{h - La}$

**60** $R = \dfrac{2aE}{L} + r$     **61** $x = \dfrac{P + R^2 Q}{a - R^2 b}$     **62** $h = \dfrac{2D^2}{3}$

**63** $\quad r = \pm \dfrac{1}{2}\sqrt{\dfrac{S}{\pi}}$  **64** $\quad M = \dfrac{4\pi^2 I}{HT^2}$  **65** $\quad u = \pm\sqrt{v^2 - \dfrac{2A}{m}}$

**66** $\quad H = \dfrac{Nd^3}{a^3}$  **67** $\quad l = \dfrac{d}{2} + \dfrac{4M}{wd}$  **68** $\quad l = \dfrac{wd^2}{2(wd - S)}$

**69** $\quad t = T - \dfrac{275H}{\pi Rn}$  **70** $\quad r = \pm\sqrt{R^2 - \dfrac{2gH}{w^2}}$

**71** $\quad b = \dfrac{T^2(a^2 + 4)}{Ph}; \ a = \pm\sqrt{\dfrac{Pbh}{T^2} - 4}$  **72** $\quad a = \dfrac{b(3x - 2h)}{h - 3x}$

**73** $\quad x = \pm\sqrt{a^2 - \dfrac{v^2}{w^2}}$  **74** $\quad h = \pm\sqrt{\dfrac{A^2}{\pi^2 r^2} - r^2}$

**75** $\quad H = T^2 - \dfrac{w^2 l^2}{4}; \ l = \pm\dfrac{2}{w}\sqrt{T^2 - H}$  **76** $\quad u = \dfrac{vf}{2v - f}$

**77** $\quad S = 2\sqrt[3]{9\pi V^2}$  **78** $\quad P = \pm Q\sqrt{\dfrac{2 + A^2}{1 - 2A^2}}$

**79** $\quad h = \pm\dfrac{\sqrt{A^2 - 2A\pi r^2}}{\pi r}$  **80** $\quad q = \pm\sqrt{r^2 - rf}$

### Exercise 11, page 42

| | | |
|---|---|---|
| **1** $\quad$ 2, 1 | **2** $\quad$ −3, −2 | **3** $\quad$ 2, −1 |
| **4** $\quad$ 1, −3 | **5** $\quad$ 2, 5 | **6** $\quad$ 0, 4 |
| **7** $\quad$ 0, −5 | **8** $\quad$ −3, −4 | **9** $\quad$ 2, −4 |
| **10** $\quad$ 1, 1 | **11** $\quad$ 1, 4 | **12** $\quad$ 0, 9 |
| **13** $\quad$ 3, −3 | **14** $\quad$ 5, −5 | **15** $\quad$ −1, 9 |
| **16** $\quad$ 5, −7 | **17** $\quad$ 3, 3 | **18** $\quad$ −4, −4 |
| **19** $\quad$ 0, 4 | **20** $\quad$ −2, 2 | **21** $\quad$ 6, 9 |
| **22** $\quad$ −3, 18 | **23** $\quad$ 0, $2\frac{1}{2}$ | **24** $\quad$ 1, $1\frac{1}{2}$ |
| **25** $\quad$ $-\frac{1}{2}$, 3 | **26** $\quad$ 0, $-\frac{1}{3}$ | **27** $\quad$ 9, −10 |
| **28** $\quad$ −8, 9 | **29** $\quad$ $-\frac{1}{3}$, −1 | **30** $\quad$ $\frac{1}{3}$, $\frac{1}{3}$ |
| **31** $\quad$ $-\frac{1}{4}$, $-\frac{1}{4}$ | **32** $\quad$ −1, $-1\frac{1}{2}$ | **33** $\quad$ 2, $-\frac{1}{3}$ |
| **34** $\quad$ $2\frac{1}{2}$, $2\frac{1}{2}$ | **35** $\quad$ $-\frac{2}{3}$, $-\frac{2}{3}$ | **36** $\quad$ 3, $-\frac{1}{4}$ |
| **37** $\quad$ 4, −11 | **38** $\quad$ 0, $\frac{3}{7}$ | **39** $\quad$ 0, $-\frac{2}{5}$ |
| **40** $\quad$ 5, $\frac{1}{2}$ | **41** $\quad$ −2, $-\frac{1}{5}$ | **42** $\quad$ $\pm\frac{3}{5}$ |
| **43** $\quad$ $\frac{1}{2}$, $-\frac{1}{3}$ | **44** $\quad$ $\frac{1}{3}$, $-2\frac{1}{2}$ | **45** $\quad$ $\pm 1\frac{3}{4}$ |

**46** $\pm 3\frac{1}{2}$     **47** $\frac{3}{4}, -2\frac{1}{2}$     **48** $2\frac{1}{2}, -1\frac{1}{3}$

**49** $1\frac{2}{3}, -1\frac{3}{4}$     **50** $2\frac{1}{3}, 1\frac{1}{6}$

## Exercise 12, page 47

**1** $16; (a+4)^2$     **2** $25; (b+5)^2$     **3** $4; (c-2)^2$

**4** $9; (d-3)^2$     **5** $6\frac{1}{4}; \left(x+2\frac{1}{2}\right)^2$     **6** $2\frac{1}{4}; \left(y-1\frac{1}{2}\right)^2$

**7** $12\frac{1}{4}; \left(z-3\frac{1}{2}\right)^2$     **8** $1; (m+1)^2$     **9** $\frac{1}{4}; \left(n-\frac{1}{2}\right)^2$

**10** $\frac{1}{16}; \left(u-\frac{1}{4}\right)^2$     **11** $\frac{1}{64}; \left(v+\frac{1}{8}\right)^2$     **12** $\frac{1}{9}; \left(h+\frac{1}{3}\right)^2$

**13** $\frac{4}{9}; \left(k-\frac{2}{3}\right)^2$     **14** $5\frac{4}{9}; \left(g-2\frac{1}{3}\right)^2$     **15** $\frac{9}{100}; \left(a+\frac{3}{10}\right)^2$

**16** $\frac{4}{25}; \left(b-\frac{2}{5}\right)^2$     **17** $\frac{9}{16}; \left(c-\frac{3}{4}\right)^2$     **18** $16; (m-4)^2$

**19** $-3, 7$     **20** $-3, 4$     **21** $2 \pm \sqrt{6}$

**22** $-1 \pm \sqrt{3}$     **23** $-2, -2$     **24** $5 \pm 2\sqrt{10}$

**25** $-5 \pm \sqrt{3}$     **26** $3, 3$     **27** $-3 \pm \sqrt{2}$

**28** $-\frac{1}{2}, 1$     **29** $1 \pm \sqrt{1\frac{2}{3}}$     **30** $1 \pm \sqrt{\frac{1}{2}}$

**31** $\dfrac{-1 \pm \sqrt{33}}{2}$     **32** $-2, 3$     **33** $3 \pm 2\sqrt{3}$

**34** $\dfrac{8 \pm \sqrt{152}}{4}$     **35** $-1\frac{1}{2}, 3$     **36** $5 \pm \sqrt{2}$

**37** $-5, 8$     **38** $\dfrac{8 \pm \sqrt{48}}{8}$     **39** $5, 7$

**40** $\dfrac{3 \pm \sqrt{53}}{2}$     **41** $\dfrac{-5 \pm \sqrt{85}}{2}$     **42** $\frac{2}{3}, 1$

**43** $\dfrac{8 \pm \sqrt{112}}{8}$     **44** $\dfrac{9 \pm \sqrt{57}}{6}$     **45** $-2, 13$

**46** $\dfrac{20 \pm \sqrt{240}}{10}$     **47** $\dfrac{-15 \pm \sqrt{205}}{10}$     **48** $\dfrac{9 \pm \sqrt{21}}{2}$

**49** $-25$     **50** $-12\frac{1}{4}$     **51** $-6$

**52** $-3$     **53** $0$     **54** $-40$

**55** $1$     **56** $4$     **57** $9$

**58** $7$

## Exercise 13, page 50

| | | | | | |
|---|---|---|---|---|---|
| **1** | $x < 5$ | **2** | $x \leq 8$ | **3** | $x > 3$ |
| **4** | $x \geq 2$ | **5** | $x > 2$ | **6** | $x \geq -1$ |
| **7** | $x < 6$ | **8** | $x \geq 3$ | **9** | $x < 6$ |
| **10** | $x \leq 1$ | **11** | $x > 3$ | **12** | $x \geq -1$ |
| **13** | $x < -1$ | **14** | $x \geq -1$ | **15** | $x < 2$ |
| **16** | $x \geq 1\frac{1}{2}$ | **17** | $x > 3$ | **18** | $x \geq 5\frac{1}{2}$ |
| **19** | $x > 0$ | **20** | $x \leq -2$ | **21** | $x > -9$ |
| **22** | $x \leq 2$ | **23** | $x > -12$ | **24** | $x \leq -5\frac{5}{8}$ |

## Exercise 14, page 53

**1** $2x^3 - 3x^2 - 7x + 3$

**2** $6y^3 - 5y^2 - 13y + 12$

**3** $9z^3 - 31z - 10$

**4** $2a^3 + 8a^2 - 18$

**5** $6b^3 - 13b^2 + 3b + 2$

**6** $3m^3 - m^2n + mn^2 + 2n^3$

**7** $6a^3 - 8a^2b + 2b^3$

**8** $2x^3 - 5x^2y + 8xy^2 - 3y^3$

**9** $2c^3 + 7c^2d + cd^2 - d^3$

**10** $6h^3 - 27hk^2 + 6k^3$

**11** $m^2 - n^2 - 2n - 1$

**12** $u^2 + 2uv + v^2 - 1$

**13** $4a^2 - b^2 + 6b - 9$

**14** $6 + 15m - 2n + 9m^2 - 4n^2$

**15** $3m^4 - 8m^3 + 7m + 2$

**16** $2n^4 + n^3 - 11n + 3$

**17** $a^5 - 3a^4 + 2a^3 + 3a^2 - 9a + 10$

**18** $2u^2 - 2v^2 + 9w^2 - 3uv - 9uw + 3vw$

**19** $c^2 - 4d^2 + 25e^2 - 10ce$

**20** $a^5 + ad^4 - d^5$

**21** $a^2 + a - 1$

**22** $m^2 - m + 2$

**23** $x^2 + 2x - 4$, rem. 2

**24** $u^2 - 2u + 3$, rem. $-4$

**25** $m^2 - 3mn - 2n^2$

**26** $x^2 + 2xy - y^2$

**27** $b^2 + 2bc - 3c^2$, rem. $3c^3$

**28** $a^2 - 3ad + 2d^2$

**29** $3x^2 - 2x - 4$, rem. $-2$

**30** $3y^2 - 4y + 6$, rem. $-3$

**31** $a - 2b$

**32** $2m - u$

**33** $3h^2 + 4hk - 2k^2$

**34** $2m^2 + 5mn - 3n^2$

**35** $3b - 2$, rem. $-3$

**36** $3a - 1$, rem. 4

**37** $m^2 + mn + n^2$

**38** $m + n$

**39** $3u - 4v$

**40** $4m - 5n$

**Exercise 15, page 57**

| | | | | | |
|---|---|---|---|---|---|
| **1** | $6a^3$ | **2** | $18a^3$ | **3** | $12a^3$ |
| **4** | 2 | **5** | 3 | **6** | 5 |
| **7** | 4 | **8** | 4 | **9** | $\frac{1}{4}$ |
| **10** | $\frac{1}{27}$ | **11** | 3 | **12** | $\frac{1}{3}$ |
| **13** | $5a$ | **14** | $\dfrac{2}{a}$ | **15** | $\dfrac{1}{2a}$ |
| **16** | 8 | **17** | 2 | **18** | 16 |
| **19** | $\frac{1}{100}$ | **20** | $1\frac{1}{4}$ | **21** | $\dfrac{3}{a^2}$ |
| **22** | $\dfrac{1}{9a^2}$ | **23** | 9 | **24** | $\dfrac{1}{a}$ |
| **25** | 9 | **26** | 2 | **27** | 9 |
| **28** | 9 | **29** | $\frac{1}{3}$ | **30** | 0.2 |
| **31** | $6a$ | **32** | $\dfrac{3a}{2}$ | **33** | $18a$ |
| **34** | $\frac{1}{64}$ | **35** | 8 | **36** | $\frac{1}{16}$ |
| **37** | $\frac{1}{25}$ | **38** | 1 | **39** | $\frac{1}{8}$ |
| **40** | 0.09 | **41** | $\dfrac{6}{a}$ | **42** | $\dfrac{2}{9a}$ |
| **43** | $\frac{1}{8}$ | **44** | $2\frac{1}{4}$ | **45** | 9 |
| **46** | $\frac{1}{4}$ | **47** | 2 | **48** | 1 |
| **49** | $\frac{1}{32}$ | **50** | $\dfrac{2}{a^2}$ | **51** | $\dfrac{6}{x^2}$ |
| **52** | 2 | **53** | $\frac{27}{64}$ | **54** | $\dfrac{2}{a^3}$ |
| **55** | $\dfrac{12a^4}{b}$ | **56** | $\dfrac{4a}{9b}$ | **57** | $\frac{1}{5}$ |
| **58** | $\dfrac{15b}{a}$ | **59** | $4x^5$ | **60** | $\frac{64}{27}$ |
| **61** | $\dfrac{1}{a^2}$ | **62** | $\dfrac{1}{b}$ | **63** | $\dfrac{1}{c^{\frac{2}{3}}}$ |
| **64** | $\dfrac{x}{y}$ | **65** | $\dfrac{1}{xy}$ | **66** | $\dfrac{b^3}{a^2}$ |

**67** $\dfrac{a}{b^3}$      **68** $\dfrac{1}{a^3b^3}$      **69** $\dfrac{2}{x^{\frac{1}{2}}}$

**70** $\dfrac{3}{y^{\frac{2}{5}}}$      **71** 4      **72** 27

**73** $\frac{1}{2}$      **74** $\frac{1}{3}$      **75** 3

**76** $\frac{1}{25}$      **77** $\frac{1}{27}$      **78** $-\frac{1}{2}$

**79** 4      **80** 81

## Revision exercise 1, page 59

**1** $(a+7)(a-2)$    **2** 5    **3** $1, 3\frac{1}{3}$

**4** $(x-5y)(x+5y)$    **5** 1, 4    **6** $\dfrac{m-12}{12}$

**7** $x=-1, y=2$    **8** $\dfrac{ea}{k-e}$    **9** 1

**10** $x>4$

## Revision exercise 2, page 59

**1** $r=\dfrac{3V+\pi h^3}{3\pi h^2}$    **2** $(a-2b)(a+c)$    **3** $\frac{3}{5}$

**4** 2    **5** $x=17, y=10$    **6** $\frac{1}{27}$

**7** $7, -8$    **8** $x\leq1$    **9** $(3x-4y)(3x+4y)$

**10** $\dfrac{-x+16y}{6}$

## Revision exercise 3, page 60

**1** 1, 2    **2** $(4x-y)(x-4y)$    **3** $(2x-3y)(2+3a)$

**4** $H=\dfrac{V^2}{2g(1-E)}$    **5** 1.43, 0.23    **6** $\dfrac{11-3x}{4}$

**7** $-10$    **8** $\frac{2}{5}, 2\frac{1}{2}$    **9** $x=3, y=2$

**10** $\dfrac{1}{y^{\frac{3}{2}}}$ or $y^{-\frac{3}{2}}$

**Revision exercise 4, page 61**

1  $36a^3$　　　　2  $x = 10, y = 5$　　　3  $d = \dfrac{v^2 - 3gh}{g}$

4  $-0.58, 2.58$　　5  $1, 4$　　　　6  $\dfrac{4 + x}{2x}$

7  $(x - y)(x + y)(x^2 + y^2)$　　　8  $-1$

9  $x < \frac{1}{7}$　　　10  $22$

**Revision exercise 5, page 61**

1  $x^3 + 8$　　　　2  $(a + b + c)(a + b - c)$

3  $11$　　　　4  $\dfrac{y}{\sqrt{x}}$　　　5  $11.74, 0.26$

6  $1, 3$　　　　7  $m = \dfrac{6k + 2c}{3k - 2c}$　　　8  $x^2 + 2x + 2, -4$

9  $(3x - 4y)(4x + 3y)$　　　10  $x \leq -\frac{6}{7}$